Over a City Bridge

Over a City Bridge

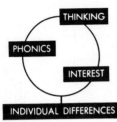

BETTS BASIC READERS
ANNIVERSARY THIRD EDITION
THE LANGUAGE ARTS SERIES

EMMETT A. BETTS

Professor of Education and Lecturer in Psychology, Reading Research Laboratory, University of Miami, Coral Gables, Florida

CAROLYN M. WELCH

Reading Consultant, Henry S. West Laboratory School, University of Miami, Coral Gables, Florida

CONSULTANT: *Hermese E. Roberts, Principal, Chicago Public Schools*

ILLUSTRATED BY: *Leon Berthold, James Caraway, Hertha Depper, Joan Esley, Elizabeth Harmon, Albert D. Jousset, Violet Jousset, Marylee Pollock, Bonnie and Bill Rutherford, Erna Ward*

Cover and frontispiece: *Oscar Liebman*

AMERICAN BOOK COMPANY

New York   Cincinnati   Atlanta   Dallas   Millbrae

7   9   11   13   15   16   14   12   10   8   6

1708613

STORIES

City Days and City Nights

In Harbor City

Little Shops

3

Signs of Spring

Busy Neighbors

Once Upon a Time in Red Oaks

4

City Days
and City Nights

Over the Bridge

"The bridge is up!" said Dick Wills.
"Look how big it is!"

Dick's father laughed and said,
"Yes, a big bridge for a big city!
Do you like the city, Dick?"

"I don't know," said Dick.
"Sometimes I do, sometimes I don't.
I like to come with you in the truck,
but I would not want to live here.
Harbor City is just too big for me!
I like our farm best."

"Look, Dick, the bridge is coming down," said Mr. Wills.

"I was afraid it was going to stay up all morning," said Dick. "Will we have time to look around the harbor?"

"Yes," said Mr. Wills. "But first I must stop at this store."

"What a high building!" said Dick.

His father laughed and said, "Yes, city buildings are high."

Mr. Wills parked the truck. "Stay here, Dick," he said. "I will be back soon."

Dick sat in the truck and looked at
the people going by. How fast they walked!
Many cars and trucks rolled by.
They went so fast that Dick could not
see the people in them!

Then someone called out, "Fire! Fire!"
Many people began to run up the street.
Dick was afraid. But he stayed
in the truck as he said he would.
Soon he saw a big red fire truck coming.
Up the street it went, as fast as the wind.

When Mr. Wills climbed into the truck, he asked, "Did you see the fire?"

"No, but I saw the fire truck go by," said Dick. "What a noise it made!"

"You are not afraid of noise, are you?" asked Mr. Wills.

"No," laughed Dick. "But I can tell you now the things I don't like about a city."

"What are they?" asked his father.

"A city is too big," said Dick. "The buildings are too high. The cars go too fast. And there is a lot of noise!"

"That may be," said Mr. Wills. "But a city has good things, too, Dick."

9

On their way to the harbor, Dick said, "Look, there is a horse and wagon!"

"Yes, you will see many horses and wagons around the harbor," his father said.

"Horses!" said Dick. "I did not know that people would have animals in the city."

When Mr. Wills parked the truck, Dick saw something. "Look!" he said. "What are all the people doing? Is there another fire? What is going on?"

Dick ran to the spot where people were standing. They were laughing and talking.

"It is no fire!" said Dick.
"The people are all looking at a cat!"

A mother cat, holding a kitten, was walking down the street. One by one she took her three kittens out of a store. Then she took them into a harbor building.

"She has a new home for them," a man in the store said. "I don't want her to leave, but she knows best."

Dick laughed. "City people take time to look at a cat!" he said. "They like animals, too. Now I know one thing I do like about the city!"

11

The City Horse

Jack was the name of the horse
that worked for Mr. Polaski.

In the daytime Jack took a wagon
up and down the city streets.
In the wagon were good things
from farms around Harbor City.

All the children liked Jack,
and they gave him apples to eat.

But Jack was not happy. He wanted
to live on a farm. He wanted to run
and play in a field.

12

Jack did not like the building
where he lived. It was a city building
with a big elevator.

After work, Jack would go back
to this building. Then the elevator would
take him up to his room.

The room was a good one, but Jack
wanted to live in a red barn.
He wanted to see green fields.
He wished he could get cold water
from a brook.

In the room next to Jack's
lived a gray horse.

"I like Mr. Polaski," Jack said
to the gray horse. "But this is
no way for a horse to live. I would have
more fun in the country."

The gray horse asked, "What would you
do in the country?"

"I would live in a red barn," said Jack.
"And I would run and play in a field."

The very next morning Mr. Polaski said,
"Jack, I have good news for you.
You are going to live in the country."

Mr. Polaski gave Jack a pat.
"I shall miss you," he said.
"But I have a new truck.
People will buy more things
from a truck."

14

So Jack went to the country.
He thought he would be happy now.

He was pleased when he saw the farm
where he would live. There was
a big red barn. And there were
green fields all around.

But Jack had no time to run
and play in the green fields. Each day
his new master gave him more work to do.

"The country is no place to play,"
said the new master. "It is a place
to work."

There was another horse that lived
in the barn. But this farm horse did not
like Jack.

"I am afraid you know very little
about a farm," said the horse.

Jack was not happy at all. More and more
he thought of his city friends.
He missed the old gray horse.
He missed his old master, Mr. Polaski.

He missed the children in the streets.
He missed the city noises and the people
who came to buy from his wagon.

16

Then one day Mr. Polaski came
to the farm. "Hello, Jack," he said.
"I have thought it over.
I like my horse and wagon after all.
Please come and work for me again."

So Jack went back to the big city.
He was happy to see his old room.
The gray horse said, "We have missed
you, Jack. How did you like the country?"
Jack said, "The country is all right
for country animals. But I guess I am
just a city horse. Now I know that
the city is the place for me."

What Do You Think?   Locating information (skimming)

Find It in the Story
What is the name of the city horse?
Who is the horse's master?
What do children give the city horse?
Where does the horse live in the city?
What three things does the horse wish?
What makes the horse happy at last?

On a City Roof

One day Dick Wills went with his father
to Harbor City. He was going to stay
a week with his Aunt Polly.

When Dick saw where she lived,
he said, "What a big building!
How will we find Aunt Polly?"

His father laughed and said,
"The elevator man will help us."

The elevator man took them up
to the place where Aunt Polly lived.

"It's good to see you," said Aunt Polly.

"Hello, Aunt Polly," said Dick.

"Here are some flowers from my garden."

"How pretty they are!" said Aunt Polly.
"I have a garden, too, but my flowers
are not as pretty as yours."

"Where is your garden?" asked Dick.

"It's up on the roof," said Aunt Polly.
"Do you and your father want to see it?"

Mr. Wills said, "I know Dick would
like to see your garden. I would, too,
but I do not have time. I must get back
to Green Hills."

19

After his father went away, Dick said,
"I would like to see your garden now.
Where are the stairs, Aunt Polly?"

"There are too many stairs for us
to climb," laughed Aunt Polly.

So they went into the elevator.
Aunt Polly said, "To the roof, please."
The elevator man took them up, up, up.
He took them right up to the roof
of the building.

20

On the roof Dick saw a green box
with flowers growing in it.

"Is that your garden, Aunt Polly?"
he asked.

"Yes, it is," she laughed.

Dick said, "I didn't know that flowers
would grow on a roof."

"You will be surprised!"
said Aunt Polly.

"Many things can happen on a city roof."

Soon a little girl came onto the roof.

"Oh, Mary," said Aunt Polly. "This is
Dick Wills. Dick, this is Mary Brooks."

"Hello, Mary," said Dick.
"Where do you live?"

"My brother and I live right here
in this building," said Mary.
"If he doesn't come upstairs soon,
he will be too late."

"Too late for what?" asked Dick.

"You will see what happens," said Mary.

Just then a boy walked over to them.

"Here's my brother now," said Mary.
"Dick, this is my brother George."

"Hello, Dick," said George. "You are
just in time to help feed our pigeons."

A clock on a high building called
the time. As it did, gray pigeons
came flying to the roof.

"Can city pigeons tell time?" Dick asked.

George laughed. "They know when it's
time to eat," he said. "So I guess
they can tell time."

Dick laughed, too. "Flowers in a box!"
he said. "And birds that tell time!
Funny things do happen on a city roof!"

23

The Flying Balloon

"Buy a balloon! Buy a balloon!"
called the balloon man.

Every day he walked up and down
the city street with his balloons.
As he walked, he called,
"Red balloons! Blue balloons!
Balloons of every color!"

One little red balloon was not happy.
It wanted to go places and do things.
So one day the little red balloon said,

"What a good day
For flying away!"

And away it sailed in the wind.

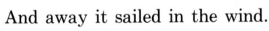

The man looked up
at the jolly red balloon.

"Come back! Come back!" he called.
But the jolly balloon answered,

"Not today!

I am flying away."

Over the city sailed the jolly red balloon.
It sailed over the buildings and the parks.

As it sailed, it called,

"It's a good day

To be flying away!"

Soon the balloon sailed
over the harbor. There it saw
a little red house. High on the house
was a big light that worked day and night.

Pigeons were playing on the roof
of the lighthouse.

When they saw the balloon, they
called, "Hello! Come down
to the lighthouse and play!"

But the wind pulled the balloon away.

As it went, the balloon answered,

"Not today!

I am flying away!"

And off it sailed to the country.

It sailed over country roads. It sailed over trees and over fields.

In one of the fields it saw some fat brown cows. How happy the cows looked! Everything in the country looked happy.

But the jolly balloon sailed on. Then it began to go down, down, down. It went down so far that it was caught in a big apple tree.

The balloon pulled and PULLED. But it could not get away from the tree.

The balloon said,

"Now I cannot fly away.

I am caught.

I will have to stay."

27

The balloon looked down at the field
and the cows. It looked down
at a big red barn and a yellow house.

It saw a man come out of the house
with a basket on his arm.

The man climbed the apple tree.
One by one he put the round red apples
into his basket. Then he saw the balloon.

"What a funny apple!" laughed the man.
"How round and red it is!"

He pulled the balloon from the tree
and put it into his basket. Then he
went back to the house.

28

On the way the man met his little boy.
"Here is a big round apple for you,"
he said. He handed the red balloon
to the little boy.

The boy looked surprised. He said,
"A balloon! Where did you find it?"

"It was caught in our apple tree,"
answered the man.

The little boy took the balloon and
began to play with it. He was so happy
that he made the balloon happy, too.

Then the jolly red balloon said,

"Here I will stay.

I will not fly away.

It is more fun to play."

What Do You Think?   Fact and fantasy

What Can Happen? What Cannot Happen?
  A balloon can sail away in the wind.
  A balloon can look down on a harbor.
  Pigeons can fly to a lighthouse roof.
  A balloon can get caught in a tree.
  A little boy can make a balloon happy.

The Harbor

One day Aunt Polly took Dick and
his friends to see the harbor.
Mary and George Brooks went.
So did one of their friends, Ted Fielding,
who met them at the elevator.

"Let's take the bus to the bridge,"
said Ted. "You can see the harbor best
from the bridge."

"Come on," said George, turning to Dick.
"I can show you where to get the bus."

"My! City boys know a lot,"
Dick thought.

The bus took them to the bridge.
It was a very big one that went
right over the harbor.

Many cars and trucks went
across the bridge. There was a place
where people could walk across, too.

"Let's walk across," said George.
"We can see more that way."

So Aunt Polly and the children climbed
off the bus and walked onto the bridge.

For a long time they stood and looked
down on the harbor.

31

What a lot there was to see!
A little red lighthouse stood in the
harbor. There were boats everywhere.

"The little brown boats are fishing
boats," said George. "Men go out
in them every day to catch fish."

"Look at the sailboats," said Dick.

"Yes," said Ted. "People go sailing
in them just for fun."

"What are the little black and
red boats?" asked Dick.

George answered, "They are work boats.
They pull things around the harbor.
Sometimes they pull the big boats, too."

"City boys know everything," said Dick.

"Not everything," said Aunt Polly.

While they stood there, Dick looked
down across the harbor.

"Look there!" he said. "Look at all
the men working on that big boat!
Let's go down and watch them. I want
to find out what they are doing."

So Aunt Polly and the children
walked across the bridge to the boat.
For a while they stood and watched.

"We have a lot to do," a workman said.
"We must get a lot of things on this boat
if it's going to sail tonight."

Suddenly three cows ran out
of a building. A fat man ran after them.

"Stop the cows!" he called.
"Help me round them up!"

"Runaway cows!" said Dick.
"Come on! Let's round them up!"

But the two city boys did not know
what to do. They rushed at the cows
and made a lot of noise.

The cows just ran away from the boys.

Dick was a country boy. He talked
to the cows. "So-o-o there!" he called.
"So-o-o there!" **1708613**

Soon Dick had rounded up the runaway cows.

The fat man rushed up. "Good work!"
he said. "Now I have to get the cows
on the boat. Will you help me?"

So Dick went to help the man.

"Thanks," said the man.
"I didn't know what to do when they
suddenly ran away."

Mary met Dick as he walked down
from the boat. She said, "Good for you, Dick!
You showed us what a country boy can do."

What Do You Think?   Indexing

Look For and Find

Names of four children

Names of three boys

Three things to ride across the bridge

Three boats in the harbor

Two things in the harbor painted red

Two people who rounded up the cows

The Lighthouse

A little red lighthouse stood
in the harbor. He was happy, for the people
of the little town were his friends.

All day he watched people sail
across the harbor. At night his light
showed their boats the way.

His best friend was Jack, who lived
on one side of the harbor.

Each night Jack sailed across the harbor
to take his father home from work.

Each night the lighthouse
would flash his light at Jack. It was
his way of calling, "Hello."

Then the little town began to grow.
After a while it was a big city
with high buildings. Big boats came
to the harbor from faraway places.

Some little boats still sailed from one side
of the harbor to the other. The little lighthouse
flashed his light for them.

"They still need me," he said.

But the little red lighthouse missed
his best friend. Jack was a man now.
Each night Jack would fly his airplane
over the harbor.

"I wish Jack still needed me,"
said the lighthouse.

Then one day some workmen began
to build a big bridge. They worked
for many weeks.

Soon the bridge went from one side
of the harbor to the other.

Now the people did not need to sail
across the harbor to get to the other side.
They could ride over the bridge.

On the bridge there was a bright light.
It helped airplanes find the way home.

"The people of the city do not need me,"
the lighthouse said to the bridge.
"The airplanes do not need me. You are
the one that helps them now."

But the bridge was too proud to answer
the little red lighthouse.

"Some day the people of the city may
need my help again," said the lighthouse.

So every night his light still
flashed to the big boats in the harbor.

One night the wind began
to blow. The harbor waters rolled
over the gray rocks by the lighthouse.

"I must do my best tonight,"
thought the lighthouse. "I must tell
the big boats to stay away from the rocks."

Then he looked up at the bright light
on the tall bridge.

"Jack will need your help tonight,"
he called.

But suddenly the bright light
on the proud bridge went out!

The men on the bridge began to work
fast. They had to get the light working.

"Airplanes will need the light tonight,"
said the men. "No one can find the field
without it. We must fix it."

The men worked as fast as they could.
But they could not fix the light.

It was time for Jack
to fly home in his airplane.
But there was no light
on the tall bridge to help him.
The little lighthouse felt afraid.
"I am not very tall," he thought.
"But maybe I can help Jack.
I helped him when he was a boy, and
I can still help him."
So the lighthouse began to flash
his light up high.
"Flash! Flash! Flash!" went the light.
Soon Jack's airplane was over the harbor.
At first Jack did not know where he was.
He made three turns over the harbor,
rocking from side to side.
Then he saw the little lighthouse.
"Flash! Flash! Flash!" went the light.
It was telling him, "You are home!"

Suddenly one of the men said, "Look!
Jack is flying across the harbor!"

"Flash! Flash!" said the lighthouse.

Then down, down, down came
the airplane onto the field.

Jack jumped out of his airplane and ran
to the bridge. He wanted to tell the men
to fix the light for other airplanes.

"We are fixing it," they said.
"How did you find your way without a light?"

"I saw the lighthouse flashing,"
said Jack. "At first I felt afraid,
but that light was all I needed.
The lighthouse and I are old friends."

How proud the little lighthouse felt!
He was there when Jack needed him.

What Do You Think?　　　　　　　　　Compound words

　　Jack saw a light flashing from a ＿＿＿ .
　　Jack saw the harbor from the air in his ＿＿＿ .
　　When work began on the big bridge,
　　many ＿＿＿ were needed.

Home at Last

It was Dick's last day in Harbor City.
He was going home on the train.
But first he wanted to buy a present
for his mother.

"You can find a good present
at the City Fair," said Aunt Polly.
"It's one of our big city stores."

When they came to the store, Dick said,
"I want to look in the windows first."

There were many windows with coats,
hats, shoes, and toys in them.
Dick looked in all the windows.

"Look," he said. "There's a handbag
with flowers on it. Mother would like it."

Dick and Aunt Polly went
into the store. They went to the floor
where the handbags were.

There a woman said to them,
"May I help you?"

Aunt Polly said, "This boy would like
a flowered handbag for his mother."

"I want one just like the one
in the window," said Dick.

"Here it is, Sonny," said the woman.
"That will be three dollars, please."

Dick gave her three dollars, and she
put the handbag into a box.

"Your mother will like this present,"
said the woman.

"Now what would you like to see?"
Aunt Polly asked. "You know this store
has many floors. We cannot see everything
in the store. But we have time to see
a few things."

"I want to see the toys," said Dick.

"They are three floors up,"
said Aunt Polly. "If you like, you may
take the moving stairs. I will come
and get you in a little while."

"Where will you find me?" Dick asked.

"On the toy floor by the moving stairs,"
said Aunt Polly. "Have fun!"

So Dick took the moving stairs.
It was fun to ride on them. He did not
have to walk at all. The stairs went
from floor to floor.

Soon Dick was on the toy floor.
He began to look at all the toys.

First he looked at the toy sailboats.
Then he looked at the toy cars.
One was a red fire truck.
Another was a blue police car.

"I would like to buy that police car,"
Dick thought. "But it is two dollars!"

Then he thought, "I have looked
at the toys for a long time.
I must find Aunt Polly."

So he went to the moving stairs.
But no Aunt Polly! He stood there
for a few minutes, watching the people.
Still she did not come.

So Dick went to look for her.

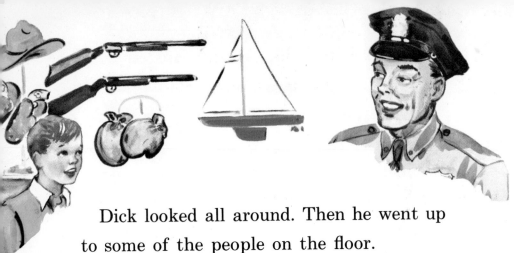

Dick looked all around. Then he went up
to some of the people on the floor.

"Did you see a woman in a brown hat?"
he asked them.

They all said, "No, Sonny. We did not."

At last Dick saw a tall policeman.
He rushed up to him and said, "Please,
will you help me? I am lost."

The policeman said, "Tell me all
about it, Sonny."

Dick began to tell his story.

The policeman said, "Don't be afraid.
This happens all the time. I know
we shall find your Aunt Polly."

They went back to the moving stairs,
and there stood Aunt Polly.

Aunt Polly said, "Dick, what happened to you? I thought you were lost."

"I thought I was lost, too," said Dick. "I looked at the toys for a few minutes. Then I came here, but I didn't see you. So I went to look for you."

Aunt Polly said, "I stood right here for a minute. Then I went to look for you. That's how we missed each other."

"You are all right now, Sonny," the policeman said as he went away.

There was just time for Dick to catch his train. So he and Aunt Polly rushed to the station.

"I had a good time," Dick said. "I like the city. But there's one funny thing about it. Everyone calls me Sonny. No one calls me by my right name. In Green Hills everyone knows me, and everyone calls me Dick."

"Soon you will be back in Green Hills," laughed Aunt Polly. "Good-by!"

"Good-by!" said Dick as he climbed on the train. "Good-by!"

Then the train pulled out of Harbor City, and Dick was on his way home. At last the train pulled into Green Hills Station. Dick was the first one off.

There were his father and mother. "Hello, Dick," they said.

"Hello," said Dick. "It's good to be home."

The station master called, "Hello, Dick."

Then the policeman called, "Hello, Dick."

Dick said, "Now I know I am home. Everyone calls me by my name."

What Do You Think?   Interpreting character

Dick Wills

How does Dick try to please his mother?
What good thing does Dick do when he is lost?
Does Dick like the policeman?
How does he please his Aunt Polly at the station?
Why does he like Green Hills?

Sounds of Vowel Letters

Say the first word and the sound of its vowel letters. Then find another word at the right with vowel letters that sound like the first word.

rain	**ai**	sail	gray	flash
how	**ow**	snow	cow	doll
out	**ou**	proud	thought	rush
coat	**oa**	caught	boat	noise
book	**oo**	rock	floor	stood
soon	**oo**	good	room	more
feed	**ee**	met	need	few

Find the Word

What do you walk on?

What is a farm animal?

What do you call a kitchen?

What do you see at the right?

Parts of Words

Say **harbor.** How many parts does **harbor**
have? What is the first part?

How many parts does each word have?

roof	answer	city	wagon
building	master	gray	men
turning	caught	jolly	happen

Say **harbor** again. Does the first part
stand out when you say **harbor**?

Now say the word **across.** Does the last
part stand out when you say **across**?

What part stands out?

about	brother	kitten	away
moving	dollar	again	penny
flashing	afraid	garden	pretty
fixing	color	broken	many

Find something to ride in.

Find a place where flowers grow.

Find part of a building.

How Many? How Far? How Long?

When man first came to our country, there were <u>many</u> wood pigeons.

Does the word **many** tell you that there were 1000 pigeons? Does it tell how many?

Now there is <u>not one</u> wood pigeon here.

Does **not one** tell you how many?

What do the underlined parts tell you?

Pigeons live in <u>every part</u> of our country. The mother and father pigeons build their home in a tree. <u>Soon</u> the eggs are there. Then the father may take his turn on the eggs while the mother bird looks for food. <u>After a time</u> they have <u>two</u> baby birds to feed.

<u>Some</u> pigeons go to a school for birds. There they are trained to fly <u>fast</u> from one place to another. The best ones get prizes for flying <u>a long way</u> in <u>a short time</u>. Others get prizes at shows for being so pretty.

Sounds You Know	New Words
ai in **sail**	wait, tail
ow in **cow**	crowd
ou in **proud**	found, mount
oa in **boat**	goat

Last Parts You Know

ee in **need**	
and **ing** of **fixing**	sleeping
u in **bus**	
and **er** of **brother**	supper
e in **met**	
and **en** of **kitten**	seven

A First Part You Know

a of **afraid**	
and **o** in **home**	alone

Find the missing word in the **New Words.**

You eat _____ at night.

A _____ may live on a farm.

You may see a _____ of people in the city.

You may be _____ years old.

In Harbor City

Whistling Friends

"There's whistling everywhere
in Harbor City!" thought Bill Hays.
    In the morning his father went
to work whistling. At night
his big brother came home whistling.
    From the roof of the high building
where he lived, Bill heard whistling.
Sometimes it came from the boys
playing games in the park.
And all day long it came from Bill's friend,
the policeman, whistling at the cars.
    "Everyone's whistling!" thought Bill.
"I wish I could!"

One day Bill wanted to surprise
Frank, his big brother. He wanted
to show Frank that he could whistle!

All day he went about, whistling.
At last he could do it! When Frank came
home from work, Bill whistled for him.

"Good!" said Frank. "And look here!
I have a present for you. It can
whistle, too."

The present was a blackbird.

"His name is Blacky," said Frank.
"Whistle to him, Bill."

Bill whistled, and Blacky whistled back.
Soon they were whistling friends.

51

Every day Bill gave Blacky cold water
and good things to eat. Every few days
he would stop at Mr. Polaski's wagon.
There he would buy a big apple for Blacky.

One day Mr. Polaski asked, "How is
your whistling bird today?"

"Good!" said Bill. "He likes his cage,
and he likes me. He whistles all the time."

When the policeman saw Bill, he asked,
"What is your blackbird doing today?"

"He's out of his cage today," said Bill.
"He likes to fly around the room."

"Don't leave the window open when he's
out of the cage," said the policeman.
"Birds like open windows, you know."

One day Bill opened the cage door
and Blacky flew out. Bill whistled,
and Blacky whistled an answer.
Then he flew to Bill's hand.

Bill put Blacky down and ran to get
his mother. "Come and see Blacky," he said.
"He flew to me when I whistled."

But when they went back into the room,
Blacky was not there.

"Oh!" said Bill. "The window is open!"

"Yes," said Mrs. Hays. "I am afraid
Blacky flew away."

Just then Frank came in. "Oh, Frank!"
said Bill. "Blacky is lost. He flew
out of an open window."

53

Frank and Bill ran out of the house.
They saw the policeman and asked, "Did you
see our blackbird?"

"No," answered the policeman.
"Maybe he flew into the park."

They ran to the park and looked. There they
saw many pigeons, but no Blacky.

"Oh, Frank, what shall I do?" said Bill.

"You must whistle," said Frank.

Bill gave a long whistle.

"Go on whistling," said Frank.

Bill whistled again. Then he listened.
Suddenly he heard a whistle from a tree.

54

"It's Blacky!" said Bill. "I heard him!
Listen! He is whistling an answer to me."

Frank listened. He heard Blacky, too.

Suddenly something black flew out
of the tree. It flew to Bill's hand.

"Oh, Blacky," laughed Bill. "We thought
we would never see you again."

Frank put Blacky into his hat, and they
walked home. As soon as Blacky saw
his cage, he flew into it.

Then Bill whistled to his blackbird.
He was telling Blacky, "I will never again
leave the window open."

Blacky whistled an answer. He was telling
Bill, "I am happy to be home again."

What Do You Think? Relevancy

Is It in the Story?

Bill Hays liked to whistle.
Blackbirds whistle best in the morning.
Bill's bird, Blacky, had a new cage.
Blacky liked to fly around the house.
Blacky answered Bill's whistle in the park.

55

No-Whistle

No-Whistle was a big new train.
He could run fast on his bright round
wheels. But he had no-o-o whistle!

Joe was a big new train, too. But he
had a whistle, and he was proud of it.

The two trains stood in the Train Yard.

Joe said, "I wish someone would buy me.
I want to run from Here to There."

No-Whistle said, "So do I. But there are
mountains on the road from Here to There."

"Oh!" said Joe. "I would blow my whistle
and go right through the mountains."

"But I have no-o-o whistle," said
No-Whistle. "I would be afraid."

One day Mr. Big came to the Train Yard.
He said, "I want to buy a fast train
that can run from Here to There."

Mr. Big looked at No-Whistle. "This is
a good train," he said.

"Yes," said the Yardmaster. "But he has
no-o-o whistle. Joe is a good fast train
with a good whistle. Buy Joe."

"All right," said Mr. Big. "I will."

No-Whistle felt very sad.

Suddenly Mr. Big said, "I'm going
to buy No-Whistle, too. I need
two trains. No-Whistle can follow Joe
from Here to There. Joe can do
the whistling for the two of them."

No-Whistle wasn't so sad now, but still
he was a little afraid of the mountains.

Soon the day came for the two trains
to start their run from Here to There.

Many people came to ride in the trains.

Mr. Big said, "I shall ride in No-Whistle."

No-Whistle felt very proud. But still
he felt a little sad. He would have to go
through the big mountain. And he had
no-o-o whistle!

When it was time to start, Joe blew
his whistle. "I'm going now," he called
as he started out of the station.
"Follow me! Don't be afraid."

No-Whistle started, too. He followed Joe
on the road from Here to There.

Joe and No-Whistle ran up and
down hills and over bridges.

At last they came to the big mountain.

"I will go first," called Joe as he blew
and blew his whistle. "Wait for me to start
through the mountain. Then follow me."

No-Whistle waited, but he waited
too long. He was afraid to follow Joe.

"There is no light in the mountain,"
he said. "The other trains would run
into me, for I have no-o-o whistle!"

Suddenly he thought, "Not all the tracks
go through the mountain. Some tracks go
over it. I shall go over the mountain."

Up the side of the mountain went
No-Whistle. It was a long pull, but
No-Whistle was not sad now.

The mountainside was very pretty.

"This is a good way to go," said
No-Whistle. "I don't need a whistle."

Joe came whistling into the station.
He blew and blew his whistle. Then he
waited on the tracks. But No-Whistle
did not come.

"What has happened to No-Whistle?"
thought Joe. "I blew my whistle to tell
him to go through the mountain."

Just then No-Whistle came
into the station, looking very proud.

Mr. Big was the first one off the train.

"That was a good ride!" he said.
"After this I shall ride over the mountain
every time I go from Here to There."

Everyone liked the new trains.
Each one thought that No-Whistle was
very brave to go over the mountain.

Joe said to No-Whistle, "Any train
that can go over a mountain is very brave.
I'm not as brave as that."

No-Whistle laughed and said, "I never
want to go any other way. You see,
I have no-o-o whistle!"

Ted and Jolly

Jolly was Ted Fielding's dog.
He was fat and round and black.
And he always wanted to play.

When people saw him, they said,
"What a jolly-looking dog!"
So Jolly was a good name for him.

What Ted did, Jolly tried to do.
Where Ted went, Jolly always tried to go.
Every morning he tried to follow Ted
to school. But Ted would never take him.
So Jolly always had to wait for Ted
to come home.

One day Ted was late, and so Jolly was very sad.

Ted tried to talk to him. He said, "I'm late because I stayed after school. We're going to have a circus on Halloween. We're working every day to get it ready."

Mrs. Fielding was listening. She asked, "Where will you get the animals?"

"Mary's cat will be a bear," said Ted. "The children will be the other animals."

"Where will you have this Halloween circus?" asked Mrs. Fielding.

"We're building a circus ring in the schoolyard," said Ted. "I will be the ringmaster because Father gave me his high hat. You and Father must come to the circus."

All week the children worked to get ready
for the circus.

At last Halloween came. Ted rushed off
to school. "See you at the circus,"
he called to his mother and father.

When Mr. and Mrs. Fielding left the house,
Jolly tried to follow them.

"Jolly doesn't want to be left at home,"
said Mrs. Fielding. "Let's take him."

"All right," said Mr. Fielding.
"He will be good because he likes
to watch animals do tricks."

Then they all left for school. Jolly
was happy because he was going, too.

When the Fieldings and Jolly came
to school, the children were in the ring.

"Now the Halloween circus will start,"
called Ringmaster Ted.

Jolly sat very still. He was happy
because he was with Ted at last.
He did not make any noise. He watched
while the funny animals did their tricks.

Then two boys pulled a cage into the ring.
A lion walked out of the cage. Suddenly
the lion jumped on Ted.

Jolly thought the lion was going
to hurt Ted. In a flash he jumped
out of Mr. Fielding's arms into the ring.

65

Jolly was not going to let any animal
hurt his master. He caught
the lion's tail. He pulled and pulled.
Suddenly out came George! Out came Bill!
Two boys were the lion!

How the people laughed!
Ted took his dog in his arms.
"Oh, Jolly!" he said with a smile.
"George and Bill wouldn't hurt me!"

George and Bill smiled, too.
"Jolly didn't do tricks," said George.
"But he is a brave dog. He caught a lion
by the tail."

What Do You Think? Sentence analysis (telling and asking)

Who? What? When? Where?
Ted gave his dog a good name.
Who named his dog?
Jolly always played games with Ted.
What did Jolly play?
Every day Jolly waited for Ted to come home.
When did Jolly wait?
Jolly went to the Halloween circus.
Where did Jolly go?

Birthday Dog

It was Bill Hays's birthday.

"Happy birthday, Bill,"
said his big brother with a smile.
"What would you like to do today?"

"Oh, Frank, let's go to the airport,"
answered Bill.

So Frank took Bill to the Harbor City
airport.

Bill had always watched the airplanes
fly over Harbor City. They looked
like birds because they flew so high.

At the airport, Bill could get close
to the airplanes. He could see them
take off and land.

"There are so many airplanes still
flying over the airport," he said.
"What are they waiting for?"

"They're waiting for their turn
to land on the runways," said Frank.
"Do you see that tall building?
The men inside tell the airplanes
when and where to land."

Bill looked up. "They must be telling
that big airplane to land now," he said.

A very big airplane was coming
into the airport. It nosed
its way down to the field.

Soon the airplane landed
on the runway, but it did not stop.
It came up the runway fast.

Bill took hold of Frank's arm.
The airplane was coming very close.
Bill thought, "Maybe it will not stop."

But at last the big airplane came
to a stop. It was so close that Bill
could see the people at the windows.
"So many people!" he thought.

Men rolled some stairs up to the door
of the airplane. One by one the people
walked down the stairs.

Bill thought, "I wish I could
take an airplane ride."

Then Frank said to Bill, "This is
your birthday. Shall we make it a party?
There is an eating place behind
that white building over there."

They went to the eating place and
asked for some pumpkin pie.
As they were eating the pumpkin pie,
a man called, "Hello, Frank."

Frank looked up and saw an old friend
standing behind him.

"Jack Waters!" said Frank. "What are
you doing at this airport?"

"I work here," said Jack. "I look
after everything the airplanes bring in.
They bring lots of things from far away.
Let me show you some of them."

Jack Waters took his friends
across the airport to a storehouse.
There they saw many big boxes that had
come in by airplane.

"See what came in today!" said Jack.

Behind one of the boxes stood
a big brown dog with a long tail.
His head and feet were very big, too.

"What a wonderful dog!" said Bill.
"Look how big he is!"

When the dog heard Bill, he ran to him.
He looked at Bill with the happy look
that a dog gives his master.

Bill said, "He likes me! He looks
as if he wants to play!"

The dog wanted to play!
He jumped on Bill, and the two
of them landed on the floor.

What fun they had!
Over and over they rolled.

71

Bill and the dog had a wonderful
time. Then Bill turned to Jack Waters
and asked, "Where is this dog going?"

Jack answered, "I don't know.
He has no home."

"No home!" said Bill.

"No," said Jack. "We have no place
to send him now. The man who had us bring
him here cannot take him. His old master
will not pay us to send him back.
We wish someone would give him a home.
He cannot stay here at the airport."

"I wish I could have him," said Bill.

"You know we don't have room
for a big dog in the city," said Frank.

"Anyway, you would have to pay
for him," said Jack with a smile.

"I have some money," said Bill.
"Maybe I can pay for the dog."

"Have you seven dollars?" asked Jack.

Bill said, "Yes, I have seven dollars.
Father gave me money for my birthday.
I will pay the seven dollars to you
right away. Then I can have the dog."

"What will you do with him?"
asked Frank.

Bill answered, "I know. I will
send him to Dick Wills for a present.
Dick has room for him on his farm.
He needs another dog."

Jack Waters said, "This is something
wonderful. Here is a boy who gives
away presents on his birthday!"

"I will not give all of this dog away,"
said Bill. "He can be my dog
when I go to see Dick.
Anyway, some of him can."

The Clown and the Monkey

Ted Fielding climbed on the bus
when it came to his stop.

"Hello, there," said the busman,
who was a good friend of Ted's.
"What do you have in that box
under your arm?"

"I will show you," said Ted
as he opened the box. He took out
a funny little clown and made it dance.

The busman laughed. "A marionette!"
he said. "Where did you get him?"

"I made him," said Ted. "He's going
to be in a play. He can do lots
of tricks."

Ted was on his way to the library.
He and his friends went to the library
every week to take out books. They always
listened to a story at the library, too.
One day they heard a story about a clown
and a dog.

"Let's give a play about that story,"
said one of the girls.

"Let's give a marionette show,"
said Ted. "I will make the clown."

So now Ted was going to the library
with the clown he had made for the show.

At the next bus stop a man got on
with a monkey. The man put his money
into the box. Then he gave some money
to the monkey, who put it into the box, too.

Ted laughed to see the little monkey
pay for his ride.

The man and the monkey sat down
in the seat behind him.

Soon the monkey climbed over the back
of Ted's seat. Ted got out his clown
and showed it to the monkey.

At first the monkey did not know what
to make of the clown. Then Ted pulled
the strings, and the clown danced.

The monkey began to dance, too,
just like the marionette.

"He's funny," said Ted. "He does
everything he sees other people do."

"Yes, he does," said the man.
"My monkey likes your marionette.
Did you make it?"

"Yes," said Ted. "I made it for
a show at the library." Then he began
to tell the man all about the show.
They did not see the monkey leave the seat.
Very soon someone pulled the string
for the bus to stop. But no one left a seat!
No one got off!

"That's funny!" said the busman.

Then he looked around and laughed.
There, up high, was the monkey.
He had pulled the string!

"No more tricks!" said his master.

The monkey jumped down and sat
on the floor under Ted's seat.

Ted and the man went on talking.
They did not see the monkey open
Ted's box. They did not see him
close it.

The bus came to Ted's stop.

"Good-by!" he called as he jumped off.

Up to the library he ran. Soon he was
in the children's room.

The tables were all pulled to one side
to make room for everyone.
Boys and girls sat on little chairs,
waiting for the show to start.

The children who had made marionettes
got ready to give the show. Ted opened
his box. His clown was not there!

"Oh!" he said. "I have lost my clown!
How can we have the show without him?"

Just then the man with the monkey came in.
The man had Ted's marionette in his hands.

"Oh, where did you find it?" Ted asked.

The man said, "My monkey took it while
we were talking. I found it after you
left the bus."

"I'm glad you found it," said Ted.
"Now we can have the show. Thank you
for bringing my clown to the library."

The children were all glad to see
the monkey. "Please stay!" they said.

"We will be glad to," said the man.
So he sat down on a little chair.
The monkey sat on a table.

Everything the marionettes did
the monkey did, too. He was so funny
that he made all the boys and girls laugh.

Everyone said it was a wonderful show!

The Seven Little Goats

In the good old days there was
a mother goat who had seven little goats.
How proud she was of her children!

One day the mother goat wanted to go
up the road to get something to eat.

"Children," she said. "I must go
up the mountain road. Please watch out
for the wolf. If you let him come in,
he will eat you!"

The little goats said, "Do not be
afraid. We will be safe in the house.
We will watch out for the wolf.
But how shall we know him?"

The mother goat said, "The wolf's voice
is not like my voice. And his feet
are black."

"Oh, then, we shall know him,"
said the children. "Do not be afraid.
We will be safe."

So the mother goat left her seven
little goats. She felt happy as she
walked up the mountain road.

"My children are brave,"
she thought. "They will watch out."

After a time, the seven little goats
heard someone at the door.

A voice called, "Open the door, children.
I am your mother. I have found
something for you."

The little goats called back, "This is
a trick! You are not our mother.
Our mother's voice is very pretty,
and yours is not. You are the wolf!"

81

Then the wolf ran to the store to get
some cream. "The cream will make
my voice very pretty," he thought.

Soon his voice was as pretty as cream
could make it. He ran back
to the little goats' house.

"Children, open the door," he called.
"I am your mother. I am bringing
something for your supper."

The little goats went to open the door.
Then they saw black feet at the window.

"We will not let you in," they said.
"Our mother does not have black feet
like yours. You are the wolf!"

82

So the wolf ran to the store again.
He said to the store man, "I have hurt
my feet. A little flour would help them."

The man put white flour all over
the wolf's black feet. Then the wolf
ran back to the goats' house.

"Open the door," he called. "I have
something for supper. I know you must
be very hungry."

But the children said, "Show us your
feet. Let us see if they are white."

The wolf put his feet on the window.
They were white now. So the children
opened the door. In jumped the wolf!

The baby goat jumped into the big clock.
The others ran under tables and chairs.

The hungry wolf caught them one by one
and put them into a big flour bag.
He caught every goat but one.
The baby goat was safe in the clock!

When the mother goat came home, she called to her children.

One little voice called back, "Mother, here I am, in the big clock."

When the mother goat heard what had happened, she went to look for the wolf. She found him sleeping with the flour bag at his side.

The mother goat made a hole in the bag. Out of the hole jumped her children.

Then they put rocks into the bag, and away they ran from the sleeping wolf.

Soon the wolf got up, ready for his supper. He opened the bag, and there he found BIG ROCKS.

That night the wolf went to sleep hungry!

What Do You Think?   Drawing conclusions

The wolf went to the goats' house because he was ＿＿＿ .
    safe   hungry   proud

The goats ran from the wolf because they were ＿＿＿ .
    lost   sad   afraid

The Horse That Went to School

Bill Hays was proud of his big brother. "Frank is a mounted policeman," he said to Ted Fielding. "Mounted police are very brave."

Then Bill began to tell about all the things that mounted police do.

"They ride on wonderful horses," said Bill. "They always help when there are big parades and crowds of people. They're the best police in the city."

Ted asked, "How do they get to be mounted policemen?"

"They go to a horse school," said Bill.

Ted laughed, "I never heard of that!"

As the boys were talking, Frank rode
up to them. "Ted, how do you like
my new horse?" he asked. "His name
is Jumping Jack."

"He's wonderful," answered Ted.
"Does he go to school?"

"Yes," said Frank. "He has many things
to learn. When a man starts his training
for this work, he trains a horse, too.
The horse school is the training school."

Then Frank told Ted that a horse had
to learn to work in crowded streets.

"A police horse mustn't be afraid
of crowds," said Frank. "He must learn
to do as he is told."

After Frank rode away, Bill said,
"I know where the school is. Some day
let's go there and see it."

So one day the boys walked
to the horse school. There was Frank.

"Hello, Frank," the boys called.

"Hello, boys," called Frank. "I cannot
stop to talk right now. Jumping Jack
is going to take his tests today."

The boys watched as Frank rode his mount
into the school.

Then Bill said. "There's one thing
I am afraid of in the tests.
Jumping Jack doesn't like to stand alone
when Frank leaves him."

Ted said, "I wish we could see the tests."

"We can," said Bill. "Come on.
Let's see what the tests are like.
Frank said they would be very hard."

Bill took his friend into the building.
They went into a big room that looked
like a circus ring. There were seats
all around it.

The policemen rode into the ring on their
mounts. Frank rode Jumping Jack.

Then the tests began.

"Watch Jumping Jack," said Ted. "He's
walking sideways, close to the people.
He looks as if he's doing a dance."

"That's called two-tracking," said Bill.
"When a horse walks that way, he can push
back a crowd without hurting anyone."

Suddenly a crowd of men rushed in.
They made a lot of noise right
under the animals' noses. They tried
to make the horses afraid.

But the horses stood still.
Jumping Jack stood still, too. He had
learned not to be afraid of a crowd.

The men pushed and pushed.
But Jumping Jack stood as still as a rock.

Ted said to Bill, "Your brother's horse
knows how to follow orders. He has
followed all the orders so far."

Bill said, "He's a wonderful horse.
But there's still a hard test coming.
It's the test for standing alone
when he is ordered to. And he doesn't
like to stand alone."

"Is that important?" asked Ted.

"It's very important," Bill told him.
"Look! The test is starting now."

All the men got down from their horses. Each man ordered his mount to stand. Then the men walked away. Two horses tried to follow their masters.

Jumping Jack looked as if he wanted to follow Frank.

"Oh, please remember," thought Bill. Then in a sad voice he said, "Oh, Ted! Jumping Jack is not going to remember."

But Jumping Jack did remember the important order. He stood still. He looked after his master. It was hard for him, but he followed orders.

Today he is one of the best police horses in Harbor City.

What Do You Think?   Sequence, main idea

1 2 3 4

Jumping Jack is a good police horse in Harbor City.
Frank gets a new horse.
Jumping Jack learns to follow orders at school.
Bill and Ted watch Jumping Jack take tests.

I Like the City

Into the city parks I go
To see my friends and call, "Hello."
The park is pretty in the spring.
The leaves are green. The bluebirds sing
And play a singing game with me.
They fly above from tree to tree.

After my friends and I have fun,
Out to the city streets I run.
And at a store as I go by,
I stop, and for a penny buy
A toy balloon so round and red.
I sail it high above my head.

91

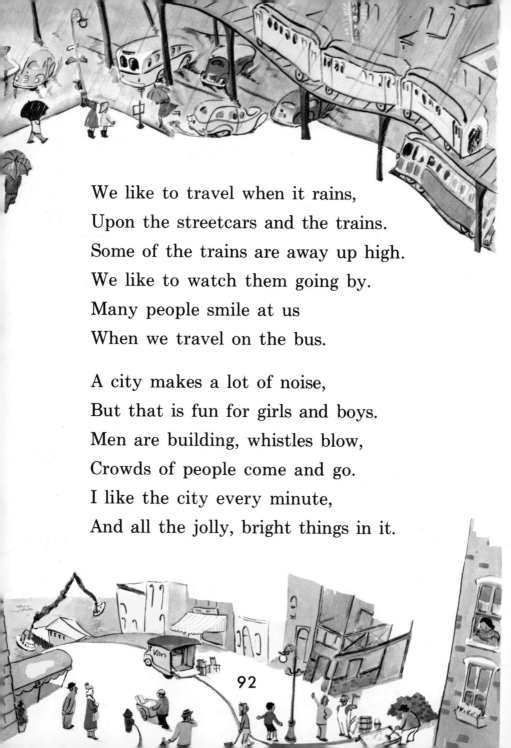

We like to travel when it rains,
Upon the streetcars and the trains.
Some of the trains are away up high.
We like to watch them going by.
Many people smile at us
When we travel on the bus.

A city makes a lot of noise,
But that is fun for girls and boys.
Men are building, whistles blow,
Crowds of people come and go.
I like the city every minute,
And all the jolly, bright things in it.

Study Pages

Sounds of Consonant Letters

Look at the consonant letters at the left.
Say the word and listen to the sound of the
letters. Then say the **Other Words** and listen
for the consonant sound.

Consonant Letters	Words	Consonant Sounds	Other Words
ck	rock	**k**	track, trick
g	got	**g**	give, goat
g	cage	**j**	pigeon, George
thr	three	**thr**	through
ch	children	**ch**	chair, chimney
tch	catch	**ch**	watch
ght	night	**t**	bright, light
c	cat	**k**	cage, because
c	city	**s**	place, voice
s	bus	**s**	send, seat, safe
s	has	**z**	always, noise

Can a goat and a pigeon tell time?
Does a cow have a pretty voice?

Last Parts of Words: er, or, ar

Say the word **mother.** How many parts does it have?

Say the words **over** and **order.**
Listen for a part that sounds just like one part of **mother.** What part is it? First? Last?

What letters stand for the sound of the last part in each word?

Here are some more words like the ones above. Say each word and find the part that sounds just like **er** of **mother.**

never   supper   master   brother

Say **harbor** and **dollar.** Listen for the part that sounds just like **er** of **mother.** What letters stand for that sound in **harbor?** In **dollar?**

What have you learned about the sound of the last parts **er, or,** and **ar** in words?

One Word for Two

1. not

The bird wasn't in his cage.

The bird was not in his cage.

2. is

The pigeon's in the barn.

The pigeon is in the barn.

3. us

Let's find the blackbird.

Let us find the blackbird.

Say each word and tell if it is made from **1. not, 2. is, 3. us.**

didn't	he's	doesn't
there's	couldn't	here's
hadn't	what's	haven't
don't	pig's	wouldn't

"_____ still time to play," said Ted.

"_____ be late for supper," called Mary.

"The _____ lost!" said George.

Sounds You Know	New Words
o in **got**	
and **ck** in **trick**	block
u in **bus**	
and **ch** in **each**	much
c in **cat**	
and **ut** in **but**	cut
th in **thank**	
and **ump** in **jump**	thump

Parts You Know	
ea in **head**	
and **er** of **over**	leather
i in **sing**	
and **er** of **over**	winter
a in **am**	
and **er** of **over**	hammer

What new word tells you:

what is used to make shoes?

what comes after the fall of the year?

Little Shops

Go-Go Finds Out

Go-Go was a funny little monkey
that lived with Mrs. Polaski's uncle.

One day Go-Go came with the old uncle
to Mrs. Polaski's fruit shop.

"Good morning, Uncle," said Mrs. Polaski.

"Good morning, Uncle,"
said the Polaski twins. "Hello, Go-Go."

"I have come to tell you good-by,"
said the uncle. "I'm going back
to the old country to live."

"What will you do with Go-Go?"
the twins asked.

"You may have Go-Go for a pet,"
said the uncle. "He is very bright.
What he doesn't know, he always finds out."

"Wonderful!" said the twins.

94

Mr. Polaski came into the fruit shop.
"So we have a pet!" he said.

"A very bright monkey," said the
twins. "What he doesn't know,
he always finds out."

Go-Go was finding out that apples roll.
The twins had to run after him and
put the apples back into the baskets.

Then Go-Go tested the plums.
He found out that they would roll, too.
The twins took Go-Go away from the plums.

Mr. Polaski said, "Go-Go is too bright!
It isn't safe to leave him alone. Don't
let him find out about my fruit wagon."

Mr. Polaski went back to his wagon,
but Go-Go stayed in the fruit shop.
He had found some wonderful bananas.

Go-Go began to eat a banana.
It was very good. So he had another.
Then he saw that the bananas were
in one big bunch above his head.
Go-Go climbed up the bunch of bananas.

This way and that went the bunch
of bananas, just like a swing.
What fun it was to swing!

Just then a woman came in with a dog.
Right away Go-Go wanted to find out
if he could ride the dog. Down he jumped,
landing on the dog's back.

The dog rushed out into the street.
He ran so fast that Go-Go could not
stay on. Down went Go-Go.

Back to the fruit shop ran the dog.
But not Go-Go! He looked around.

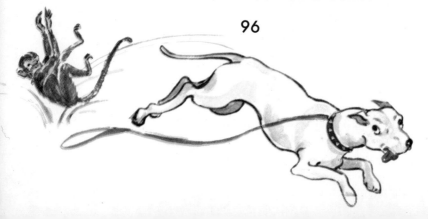

Go-Go saw an open door. He pushed it
and walked into Miss Gray's Hat Shop.

Go-Go had never had a hat. He thought
it would be fun to find out about one.

One, two, three! A big red hat was
on his head. The hat was too big.
Go-Go didn't care.

Miss Gray cared. She rushed after Go-Go.
"Come back with my hat!" she ordered.

But Go-Go jumped through an open window.
Into the street he fell, with the hat
still on his head.

He looked around for some more fun.

Go-Go saw a man holding a big bunch
of colored balloons. He wanted to find out
about them. So he climbed a tree
above the man's head. Swinging by his tail,
he looked far down at the pretty balloons.
Down fell the big red hat right on top
of the balloon man's head!

The man was so surprised that he
let go of the balloons. Up they went.
Go-Go caught them by the strings
as they went by.

The wind blew the balloons high
above the treetops. Go-Go went with them,
swinging from the strings.
It was a funny way to travel,
but Go-Go didn't care.

Over the top of the park fence
he sailed. When he looked down,
he could see many cages. He saw
cages of lions and bears.

Then Go-Go saw a cage of little monkeys
just like himself. Some were swinging
by their tails. Some were doing tricks.

Go-Go wanted to find out all
about the monkeys. So he let
the pretty balloons go. Down he fell
right into the monkeys' cage!
There he has stayed from that day to this.

Every week the Polaskis go to see him.
They always give him bananas. They like
to watch him play with the other monkeys.

"Our pet is happy here," say the twins.

"Go-Go has found a good, safe home
for himself," say Mr. and Mrs. Polaski.

99

Mr. Plum and the Little Green Tree

A little green tree stood all alone
in Harbor City. Not far from the tree
was a little old house.

In the house lived an old shoemaker.
His name was Mr. Plum.

Mr. Plum worked hard all day long,
fixing people's shoes. He liked his work.

"I hope I shall go on working for
many years," he would say to himself.

As he worked, he would sing and look at
the little green tree.

"How pretty my little green tree is!"
he would think. He felt as if it were his.

Mr. Plum hoped that the tree would live
a long time. Early each morning,
he went out to take care of it.
When no rain fell, he always watered it.

Early one morning, as he sat working,
he saw a truck stop. Three men
got out and walked over to the tree.

"What do they want?" thought Mr. Plum.
One man had a saw in his hand.

Mr. Plum went out and asked this man,
"What are you going to do with that saw?"

"Cut down this tree," said the man.

"Cut it down?" said Mr. Plum.
"Who said you could?"

"We have orders from the mayor,"
the man answered.

Mr. Plum thought and thought.
Then he said, "Will you wait a while?
I think I will go to see the mayor."

The men did not answer.

Mr. Plum said, "My home is over my shop.
Why don't you go upstairs and wait?
You will find something there to eat."

"All right," said the men.
"We're hungry. And it's still early.
We shall wait upstairs for you."

Mr. Plum went into his shop. He put
on his hat. But he did not remember
to take off his shoemaker's apron.

Mr. Plum got on a bus. All the people
looked at him. It was not every day that
they saw a man in a shoemaker's apron.

Soon he came to the big building where
he would see the mayor.

Mr. Plum rode up in the elevator.
When he got off, he saw a big door.
It had MAYOR on it in gold letters.

Mr. Plum went in. There sat the mayor
with one foot up on a chair.

The mayor was not pleased to see him.

"Who are you?" he asked. "And why are
you here in a shoemaker's apron?"

Mr. Plum jumped. He wanted to run
away from this important man. But he
thought of the tree, and he felt brave.

"I hope you can help me," he began.
"There is a tree near my shop, and . . . ."

Just then the mayor said, "Oh, how
my foot hurts!"

Mr. Plum looked at the mayor's foot.
He put on his glasses and looked again.

Mr. Plum said, "I know why your foot hurts. It is too big for your shoe. I think I can fix your shoe."

"Right now?" asked the mayor.

"I think so," said Mr. Plum. Then he took from his apron the things he needed.

He cut a hole in the side of the shoe. Then he began to sew. "I'm glad I did not take off my apron," he said to himself.

When he was through sewing, he started to hammer.

The mayor sat nearby and watched. In a little while the shoe was fixed. The mayor tried it on and stood up.

"It doesn't hurt at all," he smiled.

Mr. Plum put his hammer back into his apron. Then he remembered the tree near his shop. He told the mayor about it.

"Please, Mr. Mayor, do not let the men cut it down," said the shoemaker.

The mayor looked down at the shoe
that Mr. Plum had sewed and hammered.
"All right," he said. "Your tree will
not be cut down. I will send an order.
And thank you for fixing my shoe."

"Thank YOU!" said Mr. Plum.

The little green tree was not cut down.
What is more, each week the mayor's
men came to water it and care for it.

Many times a day Mr. Plum looked out
of his shop window and smiled.

"My little green tree," he would say.
Then he would sing to himself and go back
to fixing all the shoes.

What Do You Think?   Locating information (skimming)

Find the answers in the story.
What was Mr. Plum's work?
Why did he go to see the mayor?
What three things did Mr. Plum do
to the mayor's shoe?

The Elves and the Shoemaker

One day after school Mary Brooks got on the bus and rode to the library.

She climbed the stairs to the children's room on the top floor. In this pretty, bright room, she always had a good time. There were enough books here for all the children in the city.

Mary found just the book she wanted. In it was an old fairy story called "The Elves and the Shoemaker."

Mary sat at a library table and began the story. This is the way it went.

There was a little old shoemaker who
worked very hard. But still he could
not make enough money for his needs.

At last he had just enough leather
to make two shoes. So that night
he cut them out of the leather.

"I will sew this last pair of shoes
in the morning," said the shoemaker.

He put the leather on the table.
He took off his apron and his glasses
and went upstairs to sleep.

Early in the morning he found that
the shoes were all made. The sewing
was as pretty as could be.

That morning a man came into the shop.
When he saw the pair of shoes, he said,
"What wonderful shoes! I will buy them."

The man gave the shoemaker a lot of
money for them. It was enough money
to buy leather for two pairs of shoes.

That night the shoemaker cut out
the shoes and left them on the table.
In the morning he found them finished.

Then some people came into the shop.
They liked the shoes and were glad to pay
in gold for them. Now he could buy
leather to make four pairs of shoes.

The shoemaker cut out the four pairs
of shoes. In the night someone
finished them.

So it went for a long time. Soon the
shoemaker had all the money he needed.

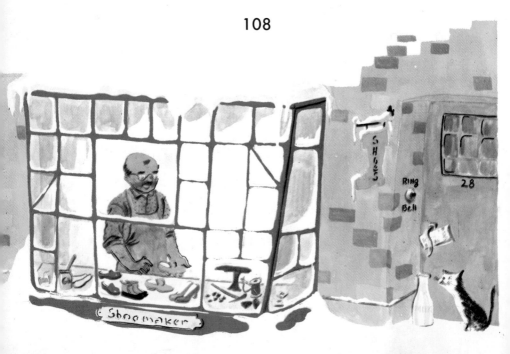

One night the shoemaker said
to his wife, "Come, my good wife.
Let us wait behind the door. I want
to see who does my work for me."

So they did not go to bed. They waited
behind the door. After a time, in came
two little elves.

The elves sat down at the table
and began to hammer and sew.
How fast they sewed! Soon every pair
of shoes was finished. When daylight
came, the elves ran off.

The shoemaker and his wife went to bed.
But the wife could not go to sleep.

In the morning she said, "The elves
are very good to us. We must find
a way to thank them."

"What can we do?" asked the shoemaker.

The wife said, "It is cold now,
and the little elves have no coats.
I will make some tiny coats for them.
Then their backs will be warm."

The shoemaker said, "I will make
some tiny shoes for them."

So the shoemaker took some leather
and made four tiny yellow shoes.

His wife made two warm green coats.

By evening the presents were finished.
The shoemaker put them on the table.
He did not leave any work for the elves.
"This evening they shall have fun,"
he said. At bedtime, he and his wife
stood behind the door and waited.

Soon the elves came in. They went
right to the table. They put on the warm
coats and the tiny shoes. Then they
began to dance. How they danced!

One step here! Two steps there!

Three steps here! Four steps there!

At last the dance was finished, and it was
time for the elves to leave. They went
up the chimney and never came back.

But the shoemaker and his wife had all
they needed as long as they lived.

What Do You Think? Main idea

What Happens?

Two elves give money to a shoemaker.
A needy shoemaker is helped by elves.
A shoemaker and his wife feed the elves.

A Home for Bingo

Mr. Goodyear's pet shop was very tiny.
In it were birds, goldfish, rabbits, kittens,
and Bingo.

Bingo was a big brown dog who needed
lots of room. When he turned around,
bingo! Things fell over. When he
sat down, bingo! Things fell over.

When he thumped his tail, bingo!
Lots of things fell over. And he was
always thumping his tail.

So Mr. Goodyear called him Bingo.

One day a woman came into the pet shop.
"I want to buy a good dog," she said.

"I have just the dog you want,"
said Mr. Goodyear. "His name is Bingo."

Bingo thumped his tail to show how
pleased he was. Over went some books
and papers.

"Oh, no," said the woman. "I want
a tiny dog for my little apartment.
I shall take that little white dog."

She gave Mr. Goodyear four dollars
and took the tiny dog with her.

When Bingo saw her go, he felt sad.
He sat down. Over went a bird cage,
on top of the books and papers.

113

The next day another woman came into the pet shop.

"I should like to buy a dog," she said to Mr. Goodyear.

"Take Bingo," said Mr. Goodyear. "He's a kind dog. He likes everyone."

"He is too big," said the woman. "I cannot have him in my apartment. I will take that tiny black dog."

Bingo felt sad. He sat down. Bingo! Over went some goldfish. Water ran over the floor.

"Oh, my!" said Mr. Goodyear. "I wish some kind people would give Bingo a home. He should have a lot of room. He cannot live in a city apartment."

Mr. Goodyear said this in a kind voice. He did not want to hurt Bingo.

When evening came, he went home.

In the morning Bingo was not
in the shop. Mr. Goodyear could not
find him anywhere!

"Bingo was listening to what I said,"
thought Mr. Goodyear. "He has run away
to find a home for himself. I hope he
is safe. I shall write to the newspapers."

So Mr. Goodyear sat down to write.
He thought and thought. At last he said,
"This should do it.

LOST

Brown dog—big and kind.

Answers to name of Bingo.

Keep him if you have lots of room.

Write to Mr. Goodyear,

Goodyear's Pet Shop, Harbor City."

115

The next day all the Harbor City
newspapers told about Bingo.
The newspapers were sent everywhere.

One of them was sent to a big house
far away from the city. In this house
lived a jolly little woman. Her name
was Mrs. Bunch, and she lived all alone.

She had a big red doghouse in her yard.
But she had no dog. There was a sign
on the doghouse that said DOGHOUSE TO LET.

Mrs. Bunch opened her newspaper and
looked at the Lost and Found news.

"My," she said when she saw the news
about Bingo. "I should like to have
Bingo. A big dog is just what I need.
I could keep him in the doghouse."

Just then Mrs. Bunch heard something
outside. She jumped up. Right in front
of her house stood a big brown dog.

"Maybe that's Bingo," she said.
"If it is Bingo, I shall keep him."

Then she called, "Are you Bingo?"

The dog barked.

"Come here, Bingo," called Mrs. Bunch.

The dog barked again and ran to her.
It WAS Bingo!

"Wait a minute," said Mrs. Bunch.
She went to the doghouse and took down
the sign that said DOGHOUSE TO LET.

"I don't need this sign any more,"
she told Bingo. "This is your house now.
Come, Bingo. You must be hungry."

Mrs. Bunch took Bingo through the front
door into her house. In her big front
room she gave him something good to eat.

While he was eating, Mrs. Bunch sat down
to write Mr. Goodyear. At last she had
found the kind of dog she had always wanted.

Bingo finished eating and sat down.
Not a thing fell. He thumped his tail.
Not one thing fell down.

Bingo, too, had found what he had
always wanted. A home with lots of room.

Jack Frost

Jack Frost jumped out of bed one night.
He had heard King Winter call,
"Jack Frost, get up. Be on your way.
There's lots to do this fall."
Jack Frost put on his high white shoes.
He jumped upon his sled.
He landed where some flowers stood.
"Please don't come here," they said.

Jack Frost said, "Is that the way
to welcome your friend Jack?
King Winter sent me, as you know,
for he will soon be back."

Jack Frost whistled as he worked
in the tiny flower bed.
He saw the flowers growing sad.
And this is what he said:

"Winter brings to fields and flowers
a covering of white.
And you will have a welcome sleep
through all the winter night."

Jack jumped into the treetops.
His brush flashed in the cold. It turned
the leaves to red and brown. And some
it turned to gold.

Down from the trees fell good brown nuts.
But pumpkins still were green.
Jack covered them with yellow paint
in time for Halloween.

Jack called to all the children.
Each one heard him say, "Get ready
for King Winter, please. Store nuts and
fruits away.

"King Winter rides on a magic wind
from the land of cold and snow.
Across the mountaintops he comes.
He will soon be here, you know."

Then Jack Frost jumped upon his sled.
He could see the new day's light.

And as he left, he called, "Good-by!
I'll come again some night."

What Do You Think? Sequence

1 2 3 4 5

Flowers were sad.
Jack Frost told the children that winter was coming.
King Winter called Jack Frost.
Leaves turned color.
Jack Frost put on high white shoes.

Christmas Magic

Next door to Mr. Plum's shop was another shop that had a sign,

UNCLE JOE THE TOYMAN

In his shop Uncle Joe had all kinds of toys that he made himself. He made dolls and clowns and boats. He made toy animals, too.

All children were welcome in Uncle Joe's shop. George and Mary Brooks and Ted Fielding liked the shop. They liked to watch Uncle Joe cut toys out of wood.

Now Christmas was coming.

Uncle Joe had to work fast because he had so much to do.

One day the three children took
a new friend to the toy shop. His name
was John Gray.

Uncle Joe called a jolly welcome.
He was seated at his work table.

The table was covered with the things
he needed to make Christmas toys.
There were strings and wood and leather.
There were paints and brushes, too.

Uncle Joe had a brush in his hand.
He was painting a little bear.

"When will our Christmas toys be ready?"
George asked.

"By the time Santa Claus gets here,"
answered Uncle Joe with a smile.

"Could I have a bear like that one?"
Ted asked.

"Could I have a boat?" said George.

"Could I have a doll bed?" Mary asked.

"I believe so," said Uncle Joe.

The three children showed John
a big covered box.

"That's Uncle Joe's secret box,"
they said. "We don't know
what's in it."

The children said good-by
to the toyman and went out to play.

George asked John, "What are you
going to get for Christmas?"

"Oh, I don't think I'll get
anything," said John.

"Not get anything!" said Ted.

"No," said John. "We don't have
much money. This winter we will have
a make-believe Christmas."

Then Mary asked John, "What would you like if you could have something?"

"A reindeer," said John. "The kind Santa Claus has!"

The three children thought hard. Christmas without toys would not be much fun. The next day they went to see Uncle Joe. They asked him to make a reindeer for John.

"Why, I don't believe there will be enough time," said Uncle Joe. "I'll have too much to do!"

Then Mary said, "John needs a reindeer much more than I need a new doll bed."

Ted said, "Well, I don't need a bear so much. John needs a reindeer more."

George said, "He needs a reindeer much more than I need a boat."

"Well, well, well!" said Uncle Joe. "I will think about it."
And that was all he would say.

Time went fast. There were just a few days left until Christmas. The three children could not wait another day. They went back to the toy shop.

"Come here," said Uncle Joe. Then he went over to his secret box and opened it. There was a little reindeer made of wood!

127

"This is for John," said Uncle Joe.

"Oh, Uncle Joe, it's wonderful!"
said Mary. "How did you find time
to make it?"

"I'll tell you a secret," he said.
"Until this week I didn't think
there would be time."

"And then what happened?" Ted asked.

"One evening I found a block of wood,"
said Uncle Joe. "As I looked at it,
some kind of magic happened. The block
turned into a reindeer!"

"Do you think some Christmas elves
did it?" Mary asked.

"I don't believe it was elves,"
said George. "I think it was Uncle Joe."

Ted said, "Now John can have more
than a make-believe Christmas."

Mary said, "Well, I think Christmas
magic is the best magic of all."

A Letter from Santa Claus

My dear, very dear children,

Many of you write letters to me every Christmas. This year I'll write to you.

First I should like to wish you a wonderful Christmas. Next I'll tell you about some of the things I do.

I'll start by telling you how I happen to be Santa Claus.

As far back as I can remember, I liked to travel. I liked all the dear children I met on my trips.

So I thought it would be fun if I remembered them at Christmas.

I live far up in a very cold fairyland.
Snow and frost and ice are all around me.
It is always winter here.

My workshop is in my house, which is
painted red. In my front yard is
a big storehouse, where I keep toys.
There I store dolls and games and blocks
until Christmas.

In my back yard is a red building which
I call my icebox. In my icebox I keep
nuts, candy, fruit, and ice cream.

In my house are many papers on which
I write the names of all the children.
I keep track of every new baby, too.

When your letters come, I find your
names. Next to your names, I write
what each of you wants for Christmas.

Sometimes it is hard for me to give you
just what you ask for. But I do my best.

Now I'll tell you some secrets about my trips.
The trip I make the night before
Christmas is the important one.

But I come at other times, too. I take
toys around to the shops. And just before
Christmas I come to get your letters.
I travel from block to block to get them.

When I take a long, fast trip, I hop
into my airplane. But where there is
snow and ice, I travel with my reindeer.

Right now my reindeer are standing in
my front yard, ready for a trip.

Many boys and girls ask if I always
use a chimney to get into a house.
I do like to hop down a chimney.
But in many big towns there are
apartment buildings. They do
not have chimneys for me to use.

Then I land on the big roof tops.
I go right into every apartment
where there are boys and girls.

I use a magic key, which lets me
into any apartment where children live.
There is not another key like it anywhere.

This key will work in any keyhole
on the night before Christmas.

No one has been afraid when I have
come late at night.

I have never met a dog who did not
know my footsteps. Now and then
a puppy gives a little bark of surprise.
But he can soon tell that there is
no need to be afraid of Santa Claus.
Then the puppy goes back to sleep.

In another year, the puppy will be
big enough to wait up and welcome me.

I have always been friends with dogs.
They always welcome me when I come,
but they never bark.

They are glad to see me leave presents.
And they thump the floor with their tails.

Letters to Santa Claus are not like
other letters. Remember to sign them,
but do not put them into a letter box.

You may leave letters by the fireplace.
You could put them on a table or give them
to your mothers or fathers.

All the big people in your family
will know where to put your letters.
Every family knows who Santa Claus is.

Before I finish, I want to tell you
one more thing. I may not come very early.
But I have never been too late.

Is it hard for you to wait for Christmas?
Here is a secret. Believe it or not,
it's hard for me and my reindeer to wait.

And now, dear children, I must close
this letter and hop into bed.

A jolly Christmas to you, and good-by.

Your dear friend,
Santa Claus

134

Study Pages

Vowels with r

Say the first word and the sound of its vowel letter with **r.**

Then find another word at the right with vowel letters that sound like the first word.

arm	**ar**	bark	pay	care
fair	**air**	than	pair	bear
there	**ere**	were	here	where
year	**ear**	bear	hard	dear
store	**ore**	front	voice	more
our	**our**	flour	four	your
heard	**ear**	learn	near	her
bird	**ir**	swing	first	fire
turn	**ur**	brush	hurt	aunt

· What word tells:

    what you do in school?

    the noise a dog makes?

    two of a kind?

    what three and one make?

First Parts of Words

a

Say **about** and listen for its two parts. What is the sound of the first part? What letter stands for that sound?

Say the word **about** again. Say the last part alone. With what letter does the last part start?

Now say each word and listen to its parts.

across   afraid   alone

What is the sound of the first part of a word starting with **a?**

With what kind of letter does the next part start —a consonant or a vowel?

be

Say each word and listen to its parts.

because   before   believe

What is the sound of the first part of a word starting with **be?**

With what kind of letter does the next part start —a consonant or a vowel?

Which One?

apartment   **1** A large room to live in. **2** A kind of building in which there are many floors of rooms for people to live in.

bark   **1** A noise made by a dog. **2** To make a kind of noise. **3** The outside part of a tree.

sign   **1** To write one's name on something; as, to *sign* a letter. **2** Words telling something for all to see; as, a *sign* on a store, saying "Closed."

think   **1** To give thought to something; as, to *think* about something before answering. **2** To believe something will happen; as, to *think* it will snow. **3** To remember, as, to *think* about a friend who is away.

How is each word used?

apartment, p. 113, p. 114, p. 132

bark, p. 117, p. 133

sign, p. 116, p. 117, p. 123, p. 134

think, p. 100, p. 104, p. 128

Sounds You Know	New Words
ar in **bark**	March, dark
or in **for**	storm, corn
ear in **dear**	clear
our in **flour**	hour
ire in **fire**	tire

Parts You Know

a of **alone**
and **head**   ahead
a of **alone**
and **long**   along
ur in **hurt**
and **y** of **puppy**   hurry
e in **pet**
and **y** of **puppy**   Betty

What Are They Called?

Mary, Sue, Polly, Betty

cookie, apple, pie, corn

March, May

hour, minute

Signs of Spring

Moving Day

One day Mr. Brooks said, "This
apartment is too little for our family.
Now that Mary and George are growing up,
I believe we should look for a house."

Before long, Mr. Brooks found a house
in a town not far from Harbor City.

"Lots of oak trees grow there,"
he told his family. "In the fall
the oak leaves turn red. So the town is
called Red Oaks. Here's a picture
of our new home in Red Oaks."

The picture showed a white house
with a blue door. There was a swing
in a big tree, too.

"I like the swing," said George.

"The house looks good," said Mrs. Brooks. "I know we shall be very happy in it."

Mary said, "I think Mrs. Brush will be glad to live there, too."

Everyone laughed. Mrs. Brush was Mary's cat. She had just had a family of five little kittens.

George would miss his pigeons.

Every evening they would fly to the roof, and he would feed them. But they were park pigeons. George did not own them. So he couldn't take them to Red Oaks.

George talked with Ted Fielding, who lived in an apartment downstairs.

Ted said, "I'll feed the pigeons. I'll take good care of them."

"All right," said George. "Red Oaks isn't far away. Now and then I'll come and help you feed them."

It was moving day at last. The moving
truck came before the sun was up.

Men began to carry out of the apartment
everything the family owned. They took
tables, beds, and chairs. They took out
pictures, toys, and books.

"We own so many things," said Mary.
"Can the truck carry everything?"

"Yes," said Mr. Brooks. "Everything
but Mrs. Brush and the five kittens!
We will take them in the car."

George rode ahead in the truck.
He had the keys to the new house.

Mary stayed behind to put the cat and
her kittens into the car. Mary looked
for them, but they were not to be found.

After a time Mr. Brooks said,
"We cannot wait any longer. We must
go ahead. The Brushes will have to stay
behind. By now the truck is far ahead of us."

The sun was high when the family
began their trip to Red Oaks. It was
a wonderful day, but Mary was sad.

"My cats haven't any home or anything
to eat," she said.

Mr. Brooks said, "I'll stop at a store
and telephone Mr. Goodyear. His pet shop
is near our old apartment house.
He will take care of them."

"Oh, please do, Father," said Mary.
"Mr. Goodyear is very kind to animals."

Mr. Brooks telephoned Mr. Goodyear.
He asked him to watch for a cat
with five kittens.

Mr. Goodyear said, "I'll telephone
you as soon as I have any news."

"Now hurry, Father," said Mary.
"Please hurry. Mr. Goodyear may
telephone before we get to Red Oaks."

"I mustn't hurry when I drive,"
said Mr. Brooks. "But it will not take
much longer to drive to Red Oaks.
We're on the Red Oaks Highway now.
We have just a little farther to go."

Soon they came to Red Oaks, a town
with pretty homes and big yards.
Along the sidewalks stood tall oak trees.

"Is it much farther to our house?"
Mary asked.

"No, just a little farther
along this street," said Mr. Brooks.

At last they saw the house. There
was George at an upstairs window.

"Welcome to Red Oaks!" called George
when he saw them drive up. "Where have
you been? Everything is in the house.
I sent the truck back to Harbor City."

Mary said, "We couldn't drive any
faster. We had to look for Mrs. Brush
and the kittens. They're lost!"

141

"Lost!" laughed George. "Just look on the side steps."

Mary looked. There in the sun sat Mrs. Brush and her five little kittens. They looked as if they owned the house.

"How did they get here?" Mary asked.

George said, "We took them along in the truck. Mrs. Brush had her kittens in the basket, ready to go. So we put them in the truck, basket and all."

Just then Mrs. Brush stood up. She walked across the yard to Mary. She brushed Mary's hand as if to say, "Welcome to our new home!"

What Do You Think? Opposites; Context clues

George rode <u>ahead</u> in the truck,
but Mary stayed ____ to look for her cat.
    before   along   behind

When Mary <u>found</u> Mrs. Brush in Red Oaks,
she was glad her pet was not ____ in Harbor City.
    lost   told   sent

Spring Is Just Around the Corner

There were signs of spring in Red Oaks.
The days were growing warm.
Winter would soon be over.

Every morning Peter Woods waited
on the corner for George and Mary Brooks.
He lived on their block and always went
to school with them.

Each morning Peter asked,
"Why must I put on my old winter things?
It's warm now."

"It may turn cold," his mother said.

Peter could not believe it. He thought
it was going to stay warm.

One March evening Mr. Woods said, "Spring is just around the corner."

Mrs. Woods laughed and said, "Yes, but which corner?"

She was sewing a big patch on Peter's old winter coat.

"Why are you sewing that patch on?" Peter asked. "It's March now! I'll not need winter clothes any more."

Mrs. Woods said, "I'll patch your coat anyway. You may still need it."

That night in bed, Peter felt cold.

He heard his mother come into his bedroom. She pulled the window down. Then she put more bedclothes on him.

"It's snowing," she said as she left.

The next morning it was still snowing.

"Get up, everyone!" Peter called.

"Betty! Father! We shall all be late!"

Everyone had to hurry. The children helped their mother. Betty put the fruit on the table. Peter went to the door for the milk and the cream. But they were not there.

"I don't think the milkman could get through the snow," said Mrs. Woods.

Just then they heard a thumping.

"Listen," said Betty. "Someone is coming. Maybe it's the milkman now."

But it was George Brooks. His clothes were white with snow.

"There are no trains today because the tracks are blocked," said George. "No one can travel to the city."

"Then Father cannot go to work," said Peter.

"How shall we get to school?"
Betty asked.

"Father will take you on the sled,"
said Mrs. Woods. "Sit down and eat."

Peter and Betty soon finished eating.
Then they put on their outdoor clothes.

"I'm glad you patched my coat, Mother,"
said Peter. "I'll need it this morning."

The children went out to play in the
snow. They were rolling it into big balls
when Mr. Woods came with the sled.

"All ready!" he called. "Hop on!"

At the corner they waited for Mary.
She got on in front, and Mr. Woods
began to pull.

First Mr. Woods marched along. Faster
and faster he marched. Then he began
to run. Suddenly he turned a corner.

Betty called, "Where is Peter?"

They all looked up and down the block.
They could not see Peter anywhere.

Then a patch of snow stood up.

It was Peter! He was covered
with snow. He looked like a snowball.

How they all laughed!

Peter brushed himself off.

"You almost lost me," he called.
"I fell off when you turned the corner."

"Sit down again and hold on,"
said Mr. Woods.

"No," said Peter. "You sit down.
We should give you a ride now."

"All right," said Mr. Woods.

The children marched along. Then
they began to run.

Suddenly Betty called, "Where is Father?"

Just then they saw Mr. Woods stand up.
He looked like a big snowman.

"You almost lost me," he said.

"The same thing happened to me,"
said Peter.

"Well, brush me off," said Mr. Woods.

"It's almost time for school,"
said Peter. "We can't stop now."

"Brush me off just the same,"
called Mr. Woods. "I can't wait until
school is over. I'll turn into a snowman."

"I hope not!" said Peter. "Spring is
just around the corner. You know what
happens to snowmen in the springtime!"

The Storm

It snowed all night and all the next
day in Red Oaks. The town looked just
the same as the day before.

Peter Woods thought, "What a storm!
Nothing but snow and ice everywhere!"
He put on his coat and ran up the block
to find George Brooks.

"What are you doing, George?" he called.

"Nothing!" said George. "Let's play."

So the boys made snowballs until they
were covered with snow. Then they went
to Peter's house.

"Where's Father?" Peter asked.

"He's helping to clear the roads,"
answered Mrs. Woods. "He's out with
the workers on the highway truck."

Just then they heard the telephone
ring. Mrs. Woods answered it.

"John King's mother needs help,"
she said. "She has nothing in the house
for the baby to eat or drink."

"Why doesn't she send John to the store
for something?" asked George.

"He went to his aunt's house on the
other side of town," said Mrs. Woods.
"Now he isn't sure when he can get home.
He will have to stay until it clears up."

She put cans of milk and some bread
into a bag. "Take them to Mrs. King,"
she said. "The breadman and the milkman
did not come today."

Peter asked, "Have we enough milk?"

"We have enough of everything," said
Mrs. Woods. "Take this can of fruit along.
I'm sure Mrs. King can use it, too.
Betty, why don't you go with the boys?"

It was hard to walk through the storm.
But at last they got to Mrs. King's house.

"I'm the milkman today," said George.
"Here is milk for the baby to drink."

Peter said, "Mother sent this bread
and a can of fruit, too."

"Thank you very much," said Mrs. King.
"What good helpers you are! Will you
have enough to eat now?"

"We have milk at home," said Peter.
"We have beans to eat, too."

Betty said, "Peter likes beans!
I'm sure he would eat them every day."

Mrs. King laughed and said, "I hope
he will get all the beans he wants."

As they were starting home, they saw
Peter's father with the highway workers.

"Hop in the truck," he called.
"Sit with me. We are busy, but we can
give you a ride. Where have you been?"

They told about the food they had left
at Mrs. King's house. Then they told
why John could not get home.

"We're very busy," said Mr. Woods.
"But I'm sure we have time to drive over
and clear the road for John."

Mr. Woods began to swing the truck around.
And off they rode to the other side
of town where John's aunt lived.

When they got there, they saw John
standing at the window.

"We will take you home!" they called to John. In a few minutes he ran out and climbed into the truck. It did not take long to drive John home.

How glad his mother was to see him!

At last the truck pulled up in front of the Woods house. It was almost night, and all the lights were on.

"The Brooks family are eating supper with us tonight," said Mrs. Woods.

Mrs. Brooks and Mrs. Woods were busy fixing supper.

The fathers went to sit near the fireplace and listen to the radio.

A voice on the radio said, "The storm will last another day. Trains can't run. Airplanes can't take off from the airports. Some towns may not have enough food."

In a little while Mrs. Woods called, "Come to supper! Sit down, everyone."

There was lots of food. There were eggs
and beans and corn bread and pie.

Mrs. Woods said, "Each family
gave something. The baked beans and
the eggs are ours. Mrs. Brooks baked
the corn bread and the pie."

"I wish Mother would bake every day,"
said Mary. "The corn bread is wonderful."

"I like this supper, too," said George.
"But what will we do if the storm lasts?
The man on the radio said there may not
be enough food for everyone."

"We will get along," said Betty.
"We can give each other food all week."

"Yes, we can," said Peter. "I'll put in
my order right now. I would like to have
corn bread and baked beans every evening."

What Do You Think?   Solving problems

When Peter and Betty went to Mrs. King's house,
how many of the Woods family were left at home?

When the Woods and the Brooks had supper,
how many people were at the table?

Brother Rabbit's Friends

George Brooks and John King were
in the same room at school. One day they
had a surprise for the boys and girls.

"We would like to read a play,"
said George to the children. "It's
called *Brother Rabbit's Friends.*
We're sure you will like it."

"I remember that play," said Betty.
"I'm sure I heard it on the radio."

"There are five animals in this play,"
said John. "We need three more children.
Each one reads what an animal will say.
Who will help us read it?"

Up went three hands.

Then George, John, and
the three other readers began.

Brother Rabbit: Hello, Mr. Woodchuck.
I'll tell you a secret. I'm going
to play a joke on some of our friends.

Mr. Woodchuck: What is the joke?

Brother Rabbit: I'll ask them to go
fishing. But I can't tell you the joke now.
Here they come.

Brother Lion: Good evening, friends.

Brother Rabbit: Good evening.
Mr. Woodchuck and I are just going fishing.
Would you care to go with us?

Brother Lion: Yes! I'm a good fisherman.

Brother Wolf: I'm hungry for some fish.

Brother Bear: I'll be a fisherman, too.

Brother Rabbit: Come along. We shall
carry the fish home in this flour bag.
Then we can bake them for supper.

Brother Lion: Well, here we are.
I'm sure we shall get some fine catfish
here tonight.

Brother Rabbit: Oh, I don't think we
want to fish after all.

Brother Bear: Why do you say that?
On a fine evening like this, there should
be lots of catfish in the pond.

Brother Rabbit: There is something more
important than fish in the pond tonight.

Brother Wolf: What is it?

Brother Bear: Are you sure of that?

Brother Rabbit: Look into the pond.
What do you see?

Brother Lion: A big round moon!

Brother Rabbit: You are right. And there
is magic gold in it. If you catch
the moon, you may have the gold.

Brother Bear: But how can we catch it?

Brother Rabbit: Hop into the pond and
try to put the moon in this bag.
Mr. Woodchuck and I shall wait here.

Brother Lion: Come, Brother Bear and
Brother Wolf. Hop into the pond
with me. We shall try to catch the moon.
Ready! One! Two! Three! Hop!

Brother Wolf: Oh, the pond is cold!
I wish I were back on land once again.

Brother Bear: But remember the gold!

Brother Lion: Here is the moon.
Hold one side of the bag, Brother Bear.
I'll hold the other. Brother Wolf will push.
We shall soon have the gold out of the pond.

Brother Bear: Now try to pull! Pull it
out of the water and onto the ground.

Brother Wolf: Here we are! Now I'll
turn the bag over. The moon isn't here!
What shall we do?

Brother Rabbit: You must try once more.

Brother Bear: In we hop once again.

Brother Lion: Pull, everyone! Pull!

Brother Bear: The moon isn't in the bag after all. It is still in the pond.

Brother Rabbit: It is only moonlight that you see there. What a fine joke on you! The moon is still in the sky.

Brother Wolf: We can't get the moon down from the sky. Here, Brother Rabbit, take your flour bag.

Brother Rabbit: Oh, you put the bag over my head. I can't see!

Brother Lion: Just march ahead. A little farther now! We shall help you.

Brother Rabbit: Oh, you pushed me into the pond. How cold it is! Help!

All: You are not the only one who likes jokes. For once, the joke is on you!

What Do You Think? Solving riddles

Which Animal?

1. Looks something like a dog and is heard at night
2. Is sometimes called the proud king of the animals
3. Has a brown coat and can eat a lot

Spring at Last

The March days went by. The winds got
warmer. The sky was clear and blue.
There was no snow left on the ground.

The trees were green. Birds were
singing. Spring had come at last.

There were other signs of early spring.
People started to make their gardens.
They put seeds into the ground. The seeds
began to grow.

Boys got together to play ball.
Peter Woods and George Brooks wanted
to play, too. But they had no bat or ball.

"We could buy a bat and a ball,"
said George. "Only we haven't any money!"

"My father used to play ball,"
said Peter. "He has a bat and a ball
somewhere around the house. Let's look!"

They ran together to Peter's house.

"May we use Father's ball and bat?"
Peter asked his mother.

"All right," said Mrs. Woods.
"But take care. I don't want anything
broken or anyone hurt."

The two boys ran upstairs. In an
old box they found the ball and the bat.
They found a big leather glove, too.

They took the bat, ball, and glove
into the yard.

Peter put a rock on the ground.

"This is first base," he said.
"Here are the other bases. And near
the fence will be home."

George put on the big leather glove,
but his hand was too small for it.
Sometimes the glove fell off.

Peter was holding the big bat.
It was hard to hit the ball with it,
but he went on trying. "I wish we had
a smaller bat," he said.

At last he made a hit. The ball
sailed across the yard. Peter began
to run around the bases. He ran all
the way around and back to home.

"I made a home run!" he said.

"Now let me try to hit," said George.
He took the bat, and Peter took the ball.

"Just try to hit this one!" said Peter.

George started to swing at the ball,
but it sailed over his head. Farther
and farther it went, over the fence.
Then there was the noise of broken glass.

The boys looked over the fence into the
yard next door. There was Mr. Fisher's
greenhouse where many plants were growing.

The ball had broken some of the glass
in the greenhouse.

"Peter!" said George. "See what you did!"

"I did only half of it," said Peter.
"You did the other half because you
didn't hit the ball."

Just then Mr. Fisher came out. He
had been planting some seeds inside.
"What happened, boys?" he asked.

"Our baseball hit your greenhouse,"
said George. "Some glass is broken."

"So I see," said Mr. Fisher.

"We would like to pay for the glass,"
said Peter. "Only we haven't any money."

"You could work for me," said Mr. Fisher.
"I'll pay you, and then you can pay me."

"What shall we do?" asked George.

"You can dig up my garden,"
said Mr. Fisher. "It's time I got some
seeds planted. The spring rains have made
the ground soft enough for gardening."

"We know how to dig," laughed Peter.

"You may work for me an hour a day,"
said Mr. Fisher. "I'll pay each of you
a dollar and a half for five days' work."

"Then together we shall have three
dollars," said George. "Let's start now."

It was so much fun to dig in the soft
ground that an hour went by very fast.
Soon the boys saw Mr. Woods coming home.
They told him what had happened.

"You shouldn't try to use a hard ball,"
he said. "What you need is a softball.
And you should have a smaller bat and
a smaller glove of your own."

"We don't have money to buy those
things," said Peter.

Mr. Woods said, "Well, finish planting
those seeds for Mr. Fisher. Then you can
work in my garden an hour every day."

"Fine!" said the boys.

So early the next week, Peter and
George started to work for Mr. Woods.

"This work is fun," said George.

"Yes," said Peter. "And soon we shall
have our own bat, ball, and glove.
That will be best of all!"

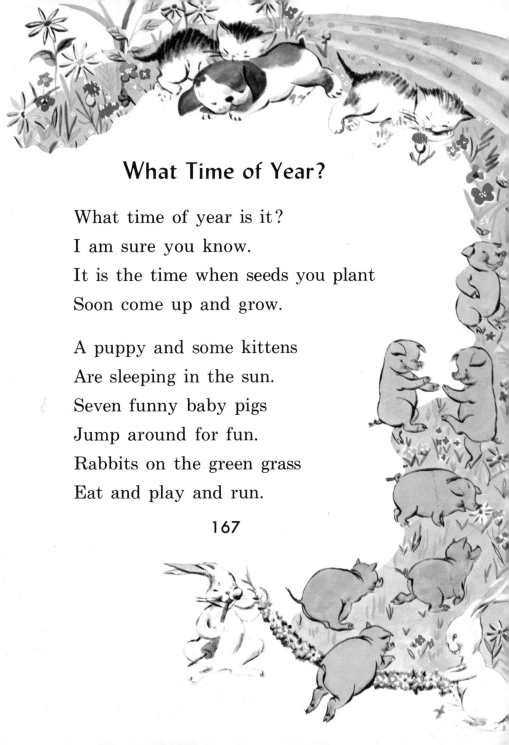

What Time of Year?

What time of year is it?
I am sure you know.
It is the time when seeds you plant
Soon come up and grow.

A puppy and some kittens
Are sleeping in the sun.
Seven funny baby pigs
Jump around for fun.
Rabbits on the green grass
Eat and play and run.

167

Through your open window
Soft new leaves are still,
Waiting for warm winds to blow
Across the high green hill.

Yellow flowers, white flowers,
And blue flowers like the sky
Grow along the garden fence.
Busy hens walk by.
They know they could fly over
But are afraid to try.

A bluebird and a redbird
Are saying, "It is spring!"
Early this spring morning,
Listen to them sing.

168

Bozo

In a grassy field not far from John King's house was a hole. The hole ran down to a secret room under the ground. Mother Woodchuck had made it.

There, in the safe little room, were five baby woodchucks. They were sleeping on a soft bed of grass. One of them was Bozo.

At first Bozo wanted to do nothing but sleep. His eyes were still closed.

But after a few days he opened his eyes. With his funny black nose he felt all around him. He was hungry.

Soon after Bozo woke up, the other little woodchucks woke up, too. They were all hungry.

Just then Mother Woodchuck came hurrying across the field. Down she went into the safe hole. Soon her children were drinking her good, warm milk.

Day by day the baby woodchucks were growing. Now their eyes were open all day long. They felt big and strong. Bozo felt stronger than any of the others.

At last Mother Woodchuck said they were strong enough to go out.

"I'll take you into the field today," she said. "But sometimes a puppy comes into the field. When I whistle, you must hurry home."

170

Soon the woodchucks were in the field.
The sun was warm, and there were many
new things to smell. Bozo smelled
the grass and the flowers.

Suddenly Mother Woodchuck whistled.
The others rushed down the hole.
But not Bozo! He wanted to stay in the
field and smell the wonderful smells.

In a minute, something covered him.
It was an old flour bag.

A strange voice said, "I'll carry this
woodchuck home to John."

Mr. King took Bozo home and put him
in a little yard with a fence around it.

"Look, John," said Mr. King.
"Here is a new pet for you."

"Oh, what a fine little woodchuck,"
said John. "I like him."

Bozo didn't like John. He didn't like
the new, strange smells. He was afraid.

Then John gave Bozo some cow's milk.
Bozo loved it. He loved the green leaves
John got for him, too. Soon he began
to love John.

At first John's puppy did not like
Bozo. He would stand near the fence
and bark. Then little by little he
learned that Bozo was one of the family.

Sometimes Bozo would follow John
and the puppy into the front yard.
He liked the soft green grass there.
And he loved the flower beds, for he could
dig in them with his strong, front paws.

When Bozo started to dig, John would
put him back behind his own little fence.

"You must stay in your own yard, Bozo,"
John would say. "Be a good woodchuck."

One day John and his father and mother
went to Harbor City together.

Bozo was left alone in his small yard.
He did not like it, for he had nothing
to do. So he began to dig. Faster and
faster went his paws. Soon he had made
a small hole in the ground.

Bozo pushed farther and farther
into the ground. Suddenly he found
himself on the other side of his fence.
He was in the garden, where he saw
many good things to eat. And Bozo loved
to eat! He ate some greens and some
new corn. He ate some string beans, too.

Then he went to call on a neighbor who
lived near the Kings.

"Well, look who's here!" said Mrs. Wheeler.

Bozo sat on her steps and ate some candy.
Then he went under the steps to sleep.
After a while he woke up and looked around.

Bozo saw a dark hole ahead of him.
He pushed his nose over the side. Down he
fell into dark, strange-smelling water!

Bozo stayed on top of the water because
he was fat. He pushed himself around
and around, looking for a way out.

Suddenly he heard John calling him.
Almost at the same time, he saw a board
in the water. He caught hold of
the board with his paws and climbed out.
There was John.

"Why, Bozo!" said John. "Our neighbor's
old well is no place for you. I'll take
you back to your own little yard."

And Bozo was glad to go home.

What Do You Think?　　　　　　　　Drawing conclusions

The woodchucks' home was safe because it was _____ .
　　　grassy　　soft　　underground
Bozo had a good time in the garden
because he was _____ .
　　　alone　　hungry　　strong

The Tree House

Mary Brooks looked up at the tree house in the big oak tree. "It's wonderful!" she said. "I have never seen anything like it before. Thank you for building our tree house, Father."

Mr. Brooks looked pleased. "You must thank the boys, too," he said. "Peter and George worked right along with me."

"We had fun," said George. "But we will have more fun playing in it."

"We will let you girls play in it sometimes," said Peter Woods.

"We will let you play in it sometimes, too," laughed Betty Woods.

"All right," said George. "We are
willing to take turns. Now it's
your turn to work."

"That's only fair," said Mary. "I'll
take the hammers and saws to the workshop."

"I'll carry the leftover boards,"
said Betty.

"I'll go and sit down," said Mr. Brooks.
"I'm tired."

While the girls worked, George and
Peter climbed into the tree house.

"This house has everything!"
said Peter.

"Everything but something to sit on,"
said George. "I'll ask the girls
to bring us some chairs."

He went to the edge of the tree house
and called, "Mary! Betty! Mary! Betty!"

But the girls did not answer. They were
busy in the far corner of the yard.

"The girls are too far away," said George. "What we need is a telephone."

"I can make one," said Peter. "I'll use two cans and a piece of string."

"I have never seen a telephone like that!" said George.

"Wait right here," said Peter. "I'll show you." He climbed down and ran home.

When he came back, Peter had the telephone. "I found a piece of string long enough," he said. "Hold this can and listen. I'll ask Mary to talk into the other can."

In a few minutes George heard Mary say, "Hello, George. What do you want?"

"Hello!" said George. "Will you please bring some chairs up to the tree house?"

"We will," said Mary. "And we will come up, too. Good-by now."

Soon all four children were in the tree house.

"We can see all around!" said Betty.

"Yes," said Mary. "I see Mrs. Brush over there."

Mary's cat sat at the edge of the yard, looking up at the tree house.

"Here, Mrs. Brush," called George. "Come on up here with us."

But Mrs. Brush just sat in the sun. At last she closed her eyes and went to sleep.

After a short time, Mary said, "Oh, look! There's Mother. She wants to talk with us on our telephone."

They heard Mrs. Brooks say, "Aren't you tree people tired? Come down and eat. I'll have something ready shortly."

While the children were inside eating,
the sky got dark, and it started to rain.

"Mother," said Mary. "Did Mrs. Brush
come into the house?"

"I haven't seen her," answered Mrs. Brooks.

"Oh, she will get wet!" said Mary.

"Not Mrs. Brush!" laughed her mother.
"Cats always find a good place to go
when it rains. She will not get wet."

In a short while the rain was over.
The girls ran out through the wet grass
and climbed into the tree house.

179

What a surprise the girls had when they looked inside! There was Mrs. Brush sleeping under one of the little chairs.

"She came up here so she wouldn't get wet," said Mary.

"Meow!" said Mrs. Brush.

"What does she say?" Betty asked.

"She says she's tired and hungry," said Mary. "But there's nothing to eat."

"We can fix that," laughed Betty. She took up the telephone.

"Hello," she called into it. "Please bring some milk up here."

"Hello," George answered. "Why do you want milk? You just had some."

"Mrs. Brush is here, and she's hungry," said Betty. "She likes our tree house. But she says she likes it best when she can be here alone. Now we will have to take turns with Mrs. Brush, too."

Study Pages

Consonants with No Sounds

Say the word **sign.** Do you hear a sound of **g?**

Say the word **hour.** Do you hear the sound of **h?**

Now see how good you are at finding consonant letters with no sounds in words.
Say each word across the line and find the same letter or letters that are not heard.

1. climb
2. who, write
3. whistle, listen
4. walk, talk, half
5. smell, ball, yellow, well
6. light, thought, neighbor, through

What word tells:

the noise you make to call a dog?

who lives next door to you?

what you do when you sign your name?

Vowel Sounds in Parts of Words

hammer   gladly   alone   grassy

Say the above words and listen for a part in each one that you say more strongly than the other.

The first part of three of the words is said more strongly. Those words are **hammer, gladly,** and **grassy.** Now say the first parts of those words and listen for the vowel sound. What vowel sound is heard in each part?

1. Find out which three words have the first part said more strongly than the last.

2. Say the vowel sound heard in the stronger parts of all three words.

Betty	smelling	welcome	ahead
winter	believe	finish	listen
horses	corner	before	shortly
papér	safely	table	afraid
began	puppy	supper	funny
mounted	surprise	mountain	crowded
along	reading	creamy	sleeping

Words with ly

1. The mother woodchuck looked <u>proudly</u> at her baby.

The word **proudly** tells you "how" the mother felt about her baby.

2. The <u>motherly</u> old woodchuck takes good care of her little ones.

The word **motherly** tells you "like" a good mother.

How is each underlined word used? Is it like **1,** above, or like **2?**

The mother woodchuck <u>bravely</u> keeps dogs and other animals away from her little ones.

A woodchuck is not a <u>friendly</u> animal, so don't try to make a pet of it.

When eating, the woodchuck may <u>suddenly</u> sit up and look around.

In the fall, fat woodchucks go into their underground homes and sleep <u>warmly</u> all winter.

New Words with Two Parts

First, use the vowel sound of a word you know to say the first part.

Then, use the last part of a word you know to say the last part of the new word.

Vowel Sound	Last Part	New Word
oo in **took**	**ing** of **reading**	cooking
ur in **hurt**	**ain** of **mountain**	curtain
ou in **out**	**ed** of **planted**	shouted
i in **it**	**en** of **happen**	kitchen
i in **in**	**ed** of **planted**	printed
i in **it**	**er** of **corner**	sister
u in **fun**	**er** of **corner**	summer

Which two ideas go together?

summer	winter	March
brother	neighbor	sister
kitchen	picture	bedroom

Busy Neighbors

The Baseball Field

Today was Saturday. Peter and George
had waited all week for this day.
They felt as if it would never come.

Saturday was the day when the boys
were going to buy their baseball things.
Mr. Woods was going along to help them
pick out their bat, glove, and softball.

Now Peter was waiting all by himself
on the front steps. He thought his
father would never be ready to go!
Mr. Woods always took his time on Saturday
because he didn't have to go to work.

After a while George came along.
"Isn't your father ready?" he asked.

"No," said Peter sadly. "I got up
early today. I did all my Saturday work
hours ago. But Father is still reading
his paper. I can hardly wait."

"Do you think he remembers about
picking out our things?" asked George.

"I'm sure he does," said Peter.

George sat down next to Peter, and
the boys waited together. They listened
to every footstep in the house.

"I hear your father now," said George.

"No, that's Mother you hear," said Peter

Just then Betty came out of the house.

"Is Father still reading?" Peter asked.

"Oh, no," said Betty. "He finished
long ago. He's looking for something
upstairs."

"Well, what?" Peter asked.

"There he is! I hear him now,"
said George.

In a minute, Mr. Woods came outside.
He had on a baseball cap.

"Oh, Father!" Peter laughed.
"Where did you get that cap?"

"I had it when I went to high school,
a long time ago," said Mr. Woods.
"If I'm going to teach you baseball,
I have to have a cap. I had a hard time
finding this one."

Just then Mary Brooks came along.

"Where are you going?" she asked.

"To pick out the boys' baseball things,"
said Mr. Woods. "Then I'll teach Peter
and George how to play."

"Will you teach us girls?" Betty asked.

"Girls can't play ball," said Peter.

"Yes, we can," said the girls.

"I think they can learn," said Mr. Woods.
"Come along. I'll gladly teach all of you."

So they all went up the street to
the store. Peter and George weren't
too pleased to have their sisters along.

The boys picked out a yellow bat,
a brown leather glove, and a softball.

"Now where are we going to play?"
Mr. Woods asked. "Our yard is too small."

"In the schoolyard," said Peter.

"No," said George. "It's closed today."

Then Betty said, "What about the big
empty lot near the station?"

"That would be fine," said Peter.
"Do you think we can use it?"

"We surely can," said his sister.
"No one uses it."

So they walked over to the empty lot.
It was a large field, covered with broken
glass, old boards, and rocks.

"We can't play here," said Mr. Woods.

"Maybe we could clear up some
of this empty lot," said Mary. "We could
take away those pieces of broken glass."

"Yes," said Peter. "George and I will
go home and get some empty baskets."

When the boys came back with strong baskets,
everyone began to clear the ground.
Soon they had cleared a patch large enough
to play on. After they made four bases,
it looked almost like a real baseball field.

"If you're not too tired, I'll teach
you how to play now," said Mr. Woods.

No one felt tired. So they played
for about an hour.

The boys were surprised to see that
their sisters could really catch and hit.

At last they got tired and sat down.

Peter said, "We could clear up all of this empty lot. Then we would have a field large enough for a real game."

"That would be fine," said Mr. Woods. "I'll telephone Mayor Smith and ask who owns the empty lot."

That very day Mr. Woods telephoned. Mayor Smith told him, "The town owns that empty lot. Tell the young people to go ahead. I'm sure they can make a real ball field for us."

The news traveled fast. Crowds of people, young and old, came to help. In a few days, Red Oaks had a real baseball field. It was named RED OAKS BALL PARK.

What Do You Think?   Definite and indefinite terms

Can You Tell?

How many years ago Mr. Woods went to high school

How many bases the children made

How long the children played ball

Red Oaks Ball Park

Now that Red Oaks had a ball park,
everyone was ready for a baseball game.
Young and old wanted to play.
There would be enough players
for two good teams.

Mr. Woods said, "Who is going
to pick the teams?"

"I think you should pick one team,"
said Sonny Painter, one of the older boys.

"All right," said Mr. Woods.
"But who will pick the second team?"

"Let Sonny pick the second team,"
said George.

"All right," said Sonny. "Let's call
the first team Red, and the second, Blue."

Everyone liked those names.

Mr. Woods picked for his team:
   George Brooks, who was Peter's friend
   Mary Brooks, who was George's sister
   Mr. Fisher, who lived next door
      to the Woods family
   John King, who owned a woodchuck
   Mr. Penny, the egg man, who had hens
      in his back yard
   Mr. Pond, the man who fixed clocks
   Mr. March, the radio man,
      who fixed radios
   Mr. Best, who was a teacher
That made nine players for the Red team.

Mr. Woods was pleased with his team.
They were nine good players.
He hoped that they would win the game.
   Sonny's team had nine good players, too.
Sonny hoped that the team he had picked
would win the game.

Sonny Painter picked for his team:

Peter Woods, who had just learned
   to play ball

Betty Woods, who was Peter's sister

Mr. Brooks, who was the father
   of George and Mary Brooks

Mr. Brown, who was the milkman

Mr. Hammer, who owned a store

Mr. Singer, who was a fireman

Mr. Bridges, who was a policeman

Mr. May, who was the station master

Everyone was busy. The two teams
worked out every evening until dark.
Other people painted seats and put up
a board fence. Mayor Smith was to open
the park on the third Saturday in May.

Peter didn't think the third Saturday
would ever come, but it came at last.
He woke up early and ran to the window.

The sky was blue, and the sun was
brighter than he had ever seen it. The day
would be hot, a good baseball day.

"Let's go out and play catch," Peter
said to Betty. He wanted to warm up for
the game, in which he would play shortstop.

He wanted Betty to warm up, too, for she
would be third baseman on the same team.

Secretly, Peter still thought, "Girls can't
play baseball very well."

They played catch until noon.
Then they got ready for the big game,
which would start early in the afternoon.

"Do you think we will win?" Betty asked.

"I hope so," said Peter.
"And, Betty, if you get a hit, remember
to step on all the bases."

At game time, the sky was still
clear and the afternoon was hot.
A large crowd waited in Red Oaks
Ball Park for the game to start.

Mayor Smith's wife had baked enough
frosted cookies to feed half the crowd.
They were the best she had ever made.

Mrs. May, the station master's wife,
had sent boxes of nuts and candy.

A storekeeper had sent ice cream, and
his wife had baked seven pies.

Mrs. Singer, the fireman's wife, had
made ice-cold drinks.

And the high-school boys who had
a hot-dog stand were busy all afternoon.

Best of all were the colored caps
which the mayor presented to each team.
He gave nine red caps to the first team
and nine blue caps to the second team.

Now they were really Reds and Blues.

As each player put on his cap,
the town band played a march.
Then the band paraded around the field.

It marched to the bandstand. Then it
came to a stop. Mayor Smith stood up.

"Welcome to the opening of Red Oaks
Ball Park," he said to the crowd.

Then he sent the ball flying out
to Sonny Painter. Sonny caught it
for the Blue team.

"Play ball!" shouted the mayor.

The game began. Mr. Woods's team made three runs, which put them ahead.

All the people laughed and shouted.

Then Sonny Painter's team made three runs. The people shouted harder than ever. The teams were tied, and they stayed tied until the last of the game.

Then Betty came up to bat. It was still a tie. All eyes were on her.

"Hit a home run, Betty!" called Peter.

The second baseman shouted, "Girls don't know how to play ball!"

But Peter shouted back, "My sister does!"

Betty could hear them. She hit the ball so hard she almost fell down. Then she heard her team shout, "Run, Betty!" She ran faster than she had ever run before. She remembered to step on each base.

She could hear the crowd shouting, "Home run for Betty! The Blue Team wins!"

Bird Banding

One afternoon Betty Woods went to see
Mr. Fisher. He was outdoors, looking at
a robin through a pair of field glasses.

"There's my old friend, Mr. Robin,"
said Mr. Fisher to Betty. "He came
from the South nine days ago.
Every spring he comes from the South
to the same pine tree."

Betty asked, "How can you be sure
he's the same robin?"

"I made sure of that by banding him
two years ago," answered Mr. Fisher.

"How do you band a bird?" Betty asked.

195

Mr. Fisher said, "We put a band on the bird's leg. We do that so we will always know him. It's hard to tell one robin from another."

"Have people always put bands on birds' legs?" asked Betty.

"No," answered Mr. Fisher with a smile. "People tried many ways before they found the right way to mark a bird."

"What was the first way?" asked Betty.

Mr. Fisher said, "Well, once upon a time, people marked birds' feathers with paint. But birds' feathers fall out. In that way the marked feathers were lost. At last someone thought of banding a bird."

"Could I band a bird?" Betty asked.

"No, Betty," answered Mr. Fisher. "Only older people may do it."

He went on to say that there are many bird banders in our country.

The Bird Banding Office is something
all bird banders know. This office
sends a number to every bird bander.
Then he marks this number on every band
he uses.

The bander first catches the bird.
He puts his numbered band around
the bird's leg before he lets the bird go.

Then the bander sends a letter to the
Bird Banding Office. The letter tells
when and where he marked the bird.

Whoever finds the bird sends the number
to the Bird Banding Office. He always
tells where and when the bird was seen.

In this way the office learns how far
and how fast birds can travel.

"Every year large numbers of birds
are marked," said Mr. Fisher.

Then Betty asked, "Where do they go on their trips through the air?"

Mr. Fisher said, "That's what we hope to learn. We know more each year."

He told Betty that birds fly far away when they leave the North.
They always fly along the same airways to the same places in the South.

In the spring they leave the South and fly to the North again. A number of them come back to the same tree.

This was the third year that Mr. Robin had come back to Mr. Fisher's pine tree.

"Mrs. Robin is on her way North, too," said Mr. Fisher. "Mr. Robin came ahead of her to find a place for their home."

Just then a tired bird flew through the air above their heads.

"Here is Mrs. Robin," said Mr. Fisher. "I can see the band on her leg."

The Pottlebys Go to a Party

The mayor was going to give a party.
Everyone in town was going.

"We are going, too," said Mr. Pottleby
to his wife and the five Pottleby children.
"And each child there may win a prize."

"Oh!" said the oldest child.

"Oh!" said the youngest child.

"Oh! Oh!" said Mrs. Pottleby.
But her voice was very sad.

All the Pottlebys looked at her.

"Who can go to the mayor's party
in old clothes?" she asked.
"Not the Pottlebys!"

All the Pottlebys were sad.
At supper they were sad. When they
went to bed they were sad. While they
were sleeping they were sad.

When they woke up, Mrs. Pottleby said,
"We may be poor! But we will go
to the party. I will try something new."

She got out her best dress, which was
very old and patched.

Mr. Pottleby got out his best suit,
which was very old, too.

Each Pottleby child got out his best
clothes, which were as old as old could be.

Then Mrs. Pottleby put on her
sewing apron. She cut and cut, and she
sewed and sewed. Soon she had finished.

Mr. Pottleby's best suit was just
right for the oldest Pottleby boy.
Mrs. Pottleby's best dress was just
right for the oldest Pottleby girl.

And each Pottleby child's clothes were
just right for the next smaller child.

Then Mrs. Pottleby dressed
her children in their new party clothes.

"Something is wrong!" said Mr. Pottleby
to his wife. "There is nothing for you
and me to wear."

"Oh, dear!" said poor Mrs. Pottleby.
"I have been sewing the wrong way."

So she cut and cut. She sewed and
sewed. She let out edges, and she made
all the clothes longer.

In half a day everything was ready.
Each suit and dress was large enough
for the next older Pottleby child.

"Everything will be all right now,"
said Mrs. Pottleby.

The Pottlebys tried on their new
party clothes. But there was nothing
for the two youngest children to wear!

201

Poor Mrs. Pottleby said, "Dear! Dear! Something is wrong again!"

Then out came the sewing machine for the third time. Mrs. Pottleby cut a piece of goods here. She sewed a piece there.

"My good machine has made the clothes shorter," she said in a tired voice.

But something was still wrong.

Mr. Pottleby said, "There are seven of us. But there are party clothes for only five. So only five Pottlebys can go to the mayor's party."

But no Pottleby would go to the party if all the Pottlebys could not go. Oh, the Pottleby house was a sad house to live in! Everything went wrong.

The day before the party, Mrs. Pottleby looked at the curtains on the window.

"What we use for party clothes is not important," she said. "See those curtains!"

Then Mr. Pottleby looked at the pretty
blue cover on the bed. "You are right,"
he said. "The important thing is
to have enough party clothes to wear."

So Mrs. Pottleby began to sew on her
machine. Soon she had finished.

The very next day the Pottlebys went
to the mayor's party. No one looked
half so fine as the Pottlebys.

No one knew that Mr. Pottleby's suit
was made from a piece of the bedcover.
No one knew that Mrs. Pottleby's dress
was made from a piece of curtain.

No one had more fun at the party
than the seven jolly Pottlebys.
And each child did win a prize.

What Do You Think?   Interpreting humor

Why Is It Funny?
"There is nothing for you and me to wear."
"Dear! Dear! Something is wrong again!"
"See those curtains!"

A Trip to Harbor City

Summer had come to Red Oaks.
The days were hot. It was time for
children to wear sun suits.

Peter and Betty Woods had been growing
fast. They could no longer wear
their last summer's play suits.

Mrs. Woods said, "Maybe Father will
drive us to Harbor City. Then we could
buy some summer clothes at the City Fair."

"I must reach my office early,"
said Mr. Woods. "I'll gladly drive you,
if we can get to the city by nine o'clock."

Next morning the children were up
at seven o'clock. They dressed in a few
seconds and rushed downstairs.

The family ate together and talked
about the fun they would have in the city.
Patches, their new puppy, watched.

"We're going to the city," Peter told him.

Patches ran out of the room.

"Let's get started," said Mr. Woods.
But then he couldn't find his car keys.
He began to hunt for them. He hunted
in the suit he was wearing. He hunted
in his raincoat.

"Where are those keys?" he shouted.
"I wonder if I left them in the car."

Peter started for the car. On the way
he found the keys. Patches was playing
with them on the back doorstep.

"No, Patches," said Peter. "You can't
go. You must stay home this time."

At last they were off. The drive
along the highway took half an hour.
Then they passed the airport at the edge
of town and went across the bridge.

Mr. Woods took his family to the store.
"Good-by," he said. "I wonder if you
can be at my office by one o'clock.
I'll take you to lunch."

"That will be fine," said Betty.

Mrs. Woods and the children went into
the City Fair to hunt for sun suits.

"Here are some marked four dollars,"
said Betty. "Let's buy them."

Mrs. Woods got the sun suits and a pair
of summer shoes for each of the children.
She got a number of things
for the house, too.

Then they had to hurry to get to
Mr. Woods's office. It was just one
o'clock when they reached the building.

Mr. Woods worked in the office
of the city paper, THE EVENING NEWS.
Every second of the day, late news was
flashed to this newspaper office.

Before lunch Mr. Woods took his family
through the building. In the newsroom
men were busy talking on telephones.
Others came in and began to write.
Then they sent the news upstairs to be
printed in the evening paper.

The printing machine was very large.
Big rolls of paper were put into it.
Then the paper passed over large rollers.
When the paper reached the other side
of the machine, it was printed.

The children liked the machine.
They liked the smell
of the wet newsprint.

Then Mr. Woods took his family to lunch. Both children were hungry, and everything was very good. Best of all were the big pieces of pie with banana ice cream.

After lunch Mr. Woods said, "I wonder if you would like to see a radio show."

"Oh, yes!" said both children.

"Well, I think I'll take the afternoon off," said Mr. Woods. "I have passes to a big radio station. Come with me."

So they went into a nearby building. They walked into a large room crowded with people and found four empty seats.

First they heard a newsman who read important news over the air.

Then a woman came out to sing.

The Woods family stayed at the radio station for the rest of the afternoon. Both children wanted to see a show called "The Mounted Police of the North Woods."

They always listened at home when the
show went on the air at four o'clock.
Now they could see as well as hear it.

They could not see any real horses,
but they could hear horses' feet.
The noise was made by a man who thumped
on an empty box. A machine made
the noise of a storm.

Both children were tired after the show.
They rested and talked as they rode home.

"I want to be a mounted policeman when
I grow up," said Peter.

"I'll be a radio singer," said Betty.

Patches was waiting for them when they
got home. All he wanted was someone
to play with right now.

What Do You Think?   Shifts of meaning

What did the Woods family do
the <u>rest</u> of the afternoon?
Why were the children glad to <u>rest</u>?
Did Patches want to <u>rest</u>?

Where the Right Shoe Was Left

I woke this morning early,
And what did I do?
I danced around the bedroom,
Hunting for my shoe.
I pulled back the bedclothes.
My shoe wasn't there.
I jumped on my left foot
And started down the stair.

I went to the icebox
And put in my head.
All I saw was seven eggs
And a piece of bread.
I climbed up on a high chair,
Looked behind the clock,
Picked up my other shoe,
And ran around the block!

Mother's Birthday Surprises

On Saturday Mrs. Woods would have
a birthday. Early in the week Peter and
Betty went to buy some presents for her.

Peter picked out a ring. He did not
pay much for the ring, but it was pretty.

Betty picked out a bunch of six tiny
blue feathers for her mother's felt hat.

That evening they showed the ring and
the feathers to Mr. Woods. He, too, had
a present, a pair of white leather gloves.

"Let's tie up our presents with this
pretty yellow paper and string," he said.

"And on Saturday let's do the cooking
and surprise Mother," said Betty.

"That will be a real surprise!" said Peter.

Saturday was a pretty summer day.
It was not too hot, and the sky was blue.

The children woke up early and rushed
downstairs to get things ready. Betty
tied on a large apron and cooked the food.
Peter put plates on the table.

When their mother and father came in,
the table looked just like a pretty picture.
The presents lay by Mrs. Woods's plate.

"Oh!" she laughed. "A surprise!
I wonder who thought of this."

Mr. Woods and the children began
to sing "Happy Birthday, Dear Mother!"

Then Mrs. Woods opened her presents.
She loved the ring and the six tiny
feathers and the pair of gloves.

"I shall wear them whenever I dress
up," she said. "You are a wonderful
family! Thank you very much!"

"You are welcome," everyone said.

Soon the plates were empty.

"My! Betty is a good cook," said
Mrs. Woods.

Then Mr. Woods said, "We will do all
the cooking today. You shall have a rest.
You must be tired."

So Mrs. Woods went into the back yard,
and there she sat all morning.

Sometimes she sewed. Sometimes she
read a book. This was the kind of rest
she had always wished for.

She wondered what the cooks were doing
in the kitchen. She could hear strange
noises coming from the kitchen.

But she could not smell any food cooking.

When lunch time came, the family
called Mrs. Woods. The lunch table
looked very pretty. The best blue plates
were on it. Next to each plate lay
a small bunch of cornflowers.

There was nothing on the lunch plates
but hot baked beans from a can. Bread
and milk were on the table, too.

Mrs. Woods knew that no one
in her family could cook very well.
She wondered if something had gone wrong
in the kitchen.

But she only smiled and said, "I never
knew a table could look so pretty."

After lunch Mr. Woods said to his wife,
"Now we shall do some real cooking.
Would you like to go to a moving picture
this afternoon?"

"Yes," laughed Mrs. Woods. "I wonder
if Mrs. Brooks would like to go, too."

Mrs. Woods telephoned her neighbor.

Mrs. Brooks said she would like to go.
She felt she needed a rest, too.

Mrs. Woods asked her family,
"When will supper be ready?"

"Supper will be ready at six o'clock,"
said Peter. "Don't take your key.
We shall stay here while you're gone.
We have plates to wash and work to do."

After Mrs. Woods had gone, Betty washed
the lunch plates. When they were
washed, Mr. Woods took out the flour.

"Now we shall bake the birthday cake!
A three-layer birthday cake!" he said.
And he tied on a large printed apron.

"I'll help," said Peter.

"I've made frosting before," said Betty.

The three cooks put flour and milk
and eggs together. They worked hard.

"Our three-layer cake will be as light
as a feather," said Mr. Woods.

When the cake was baked, it smelled
good, but it looked very strange.
Betty began to frost it anyway.

"Something has gone wrong," she said.
"The frosting runs off the cake."

When Mrs. Woods came home, she smiled.
"The fire was too hot," she said. "And
you didn't cook the frosting long enough.
But I'm sure the cake will be good anyhow."

"What's in that bag?" Peter asked.

"I've brought some food from the store,"
said his mother.

"I'm glad you brought it," said Peter.
"We were too busy to cook anything but cake."

Study Pages

Sound of u in cut

Say **cut.** Now say its vowel sound. What letter stands for the vowel sound?

Say each word and its vowel sound. Find the words with the same vowel sound as **cut.**

sun	south	bunch	plum
suit	lunch	much	hunt

Sound of o in come

Say **come** and its vowel sound. What letter stands for the vowel sound? Say the vowel sounds of **cut** and **come.** Are they the same?

Find the words with the same vowel sound as **cut** and **come.**

done	front	glove	those
from	both	once	love

Do the same with the first parts of the words that follow:

summer	number	busy	puppy
wonder	brother	monkey	broken

Last Parts of Words

Say **kitten** and listen to its two parts.
What letters stand for the last part?
The sound of what letter is heard as the last part?

Here are some two-part words that have
the same sound for the last part. Say each word.
Then find the letters that stand for the sound of **n**
in the last part.

seven   wagon   curtain
sudden   robin   station

Say **table** and listen to its two parts.
What letters stand for the last part? The sound
of what letter is heard as the last part?

Here are more words with the sound of l as
the last part. What letters stand for the sound of l?

uncle   people   travel

What is the name of a place where you wait
for a bus or a train?
What is used to make a window pretty?

Uses of Words

1. Bill ate his <u>lunch</u> at noon.
2. Bill wanted to <u>lunch</u> with his friends.

In the first sentence **lunch** tells you "something" Bill ate.

In the second sentence **lunch** tells you what Bill wanted "to do."

Tell if each underlined word is used like **1** or like **2.**

It was so dark, Jack could hardly read the <u>print</u> in his book.

Frank liked to <u>print</u> his name on all his books.

Mary said she would <u>number</u> the players for the game.

A large <u>number</u> of people came to see the baseball game.

New Words with Two Parts

First, use the vowel sound of a word you know to say the first part.

Then, use the last part of a word you know to say the last part of the new word.

Vowel Sound	Last Part	New Word
e in **dress**	**er** of **sister**	better
e in **dress**	**er** of **sister**	clever
i in **six**	**er** of **sister**	river
o in **come**	**on** of **wagon**	London
ea in **head**	**y** of **busy**	heavy
a in **plate**	**le** of **uncle**	able
oi in **voice**	**ed** of **hunted**	pointed

If you are fat, you may be ____ .

If you are in a boat, you may be traveling down a ____ .

If you want to see a city, go to ____ .

If you are seven years old, you may be ____ to read.

Once Upon a Time in Red Oaks

A Long Winter Sleep

Nuts were falling from the trees.
The days were shorter, and the smell
of fall was in the air. Sometimes
a white frost could be seen on the grass.

All the country began to change.

Bozo, the pet woodchuck, began to change,
too. His dark coat was growing heavy.

Bozo had always liked to eat. But now
he could not get enough food. Under his
heavy coat were layers of fat.

Bozo no longer followed John King and
his puppy over the fields. Bozo went
only a short way. Then he rested.

He would sit on the grass as if to say,
"I'm too tired to go any farther!"

218

One day Bozo had what he thought was a very bright idea. He felt that he needed to dig a hole. He wanted a real hole far under the ground. He just wanted to go into the safe, dark hole and sleep.

Bozo thought this idea of a hole to sleep in was a new idea. He was proud of himself.

He did not know that all woodchucks sleep in dark holes throughout the winter.

Bozo hunted for a spot to dig his hole. First he tried to dig near the edge of the henhouse. But Mr. King chased him away.

Bozo came back again and again to dig near the henhouse. But he always found the hole covered with a board.

Then Bozo began to dig a second hole in a neighboring yard. But the owners chased him away.

Days passed. Then a third hole was
found near the barn. The hole was new
and not very deep. John felt sure it
was Bozo's hole, and he was not wrong.

John soon learned that Bozo would
dig only before anyone woke up.
John was sorry that Bozo did not want
to be seen at work.

More time passed. The hole grew deeper.

One afternoon Mrs. King looked out
the kitchen window. She saw Bozo
rushing across the grass. He was
carrying one of her kitchen curtains.

She chased him and took the curtain.

"I'm sorry, Bozo," she said.
"I just washed that curtain. You can't
have it for your underground bedroom."

Every day Bozo worked on his new home.
But he was not ready to go into it
and pass the rest of the winter there.

Day after day, he would go calling.
The kind neighbors would hear
his tiny paws on their back steps.
Then they would see his funny face and
bright eyes at the kitchen door.

The neighbors helped Bozo get ready
for the winter ahead. They brought him
plates of food. Sometimes they gave him
cake and nut bread. He loved nut bread.

He loved bananas, too. He would hold
a banana in his tiny paws and eat it.

Bozo grew so fat he could hardly walk.
He still tried to run home when he heard
John whistling. But he seemed to be
thinking of other things. His face and
eyes had a faraway look. He seemed
to be thinking deep, secret thoughts.

Then a heavy rainstorm came. It
lasted a few days. It blew down leaves
and nuts. It washed the fields and roads.

While the storm blew, no one saw a sign
of Bozo. John wondered where he had gone.

Then one morning John saw Bozo's face
at the kitchen door. Bozo had changed
in those few days. How heavy he was!
He seemed to have more layers of fat
than ever.

For another week Bozo came to the
house almost every day. He would sit on
his short legs. And the faraway look
would come into his eyes and over his face.

John grew sad when he saw the change
in his little pet. He knew Bozo would
soon go away and would be gone all winter.

One day there was a snowstorm.
John hunted for Bozo's footprints
in the soft, wet snow. There weren't any.

The storm lasted a few hours more.

Snow blocked the opening of Bozo's hole.

John asked, "Will poor Bozo get enough air in that deep hole where he has gone?"

"Don't be sorry for him," said Mr. King. "Bozo will get enough air, and the snow will keep him warm."

John asked, "Is it true that he ate enough this fall to last all winter?"

"Yes, it's true," answered Mr. King. "And it's true of many other animals that sleep underground all winter."

"And is it true that Bozo will return in the spring?" asked John.

"Yes, he will return," said Mr. King. "And I'm sure he will be glad to see you when he does return."

What Do You Think?   Drawing conclusions

Why did Bozo eat so much?

Why did he try to dig the holes?

Why did he take Mrs. King's curtain?

Lost in the Woods

George Brooks liked Red Oaks.
He had a number of new friends.
But he remembered his old friends, too.

His best friend was Bill Hays, who
lived in Harbor City. Bill had never
been to Red Oaks.

One day George said to his mother,
"I haven't seen Bill Hays for a while.
He might like to come to Red Oaks. He
might stay with us for a while."

Mrs. Brooks said, "That's a fine idea.
He might come for the last part
of the week. Call him now."

George found Bill's number in the
telephone book. Then he called
"Harbor City, nine-nine-six-six."

Soon he heard the sound of Bill's voice.
George asked Bill if he could come
to Red Oaks for the last part of the week.

"What a wonderful idea!" Bill exclaimed.
"Wait a second. I'll ask my mother."

A few seconds passed. Then Bill returned
to the telephone and said, "I can come."

"My father will bring you," said George.
"He leaves the office before six o'clock."

So Mr. Brooks brought Bill to Red Oaks.
Bill was wearing a new suit and tie.

George exclaimed, "Hello, Bill! I hope you
brought a change of clothes. This Saturday
we might take a trip to the woods."

"That sounds fine," said Bill.
"I've brought my old brown suit and cap.
I can wear them."

225

The next morning both boys woke up at six o'clock. Mrs. Brooks cooked some food for them to eat. Then she gave them something for their lunch in the woods.

As the boys left the house, she said, "Don't get lost in the deep woods."

"I can't get lost," George said. "I can find my way by looking at the sun. As long as I can see the sun, I know what direction I'm going. Do you, Bill?"

"I've no idea," said Bill. "But I would like to learn."

"Well, I'll teach you," said George. "It's important to know your directions. It's no joke to get lost in deep woods."

He pointed to the sun above the trees.

"First you should point to the sun
with your right hand," George said.

Bill pointed to the sun.

"In the morning the sun is in the east,"
said George. "So you are pointing east
with your right hand. Now hold out your
left hand."

Bill did as he was told.

"Now your left hand points west," said
George. "So you face north. The woods are
ahead to the north. If you know east and
west, you can find north and south.
But you must remember one more thing."

"What's that?" Bill asked.

"The sun goes down in the west," George
said. "Your right hand must point west
if you want to face south.
Now you can find directions in the morning
as well as in the afternoon."

"That sounds good," said Bill.

Then George marked out a direction finder on the ground.

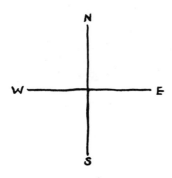

"I might be able to tell directions now," said Bill. "I hope so, anyway. In which direction did you say the woods are?"

"Toward the north," answered George.

So the two boys walked toward the north. In half an hour they reached the edge of the deep woods.

Many nut trees grew in this part of the woods. So the boys rested for a while and ate some nuts.

Then they went deeper into the woods, which seemed dark and still.

Toward noon the boys came to a clearing.
"I like this part of the woods,"
said George. "Let's eat here."

They made a fire and cooked their lunch.

Suddenly Bill exclaimed, "See that
rabbit hop! Let's chase him to his hole."

"You chase him," said George. "It's
not safe for me to leave this fire."

So Bill went to hunt for the rabbit.
He was not able to find it, but he walked
on into the woods, just the same.

He walked farther and farther.
Suddenly he exclaimed, "I've gone
too far. I believe I'm lost!"

At first he felt afraid. Then he
thought, "A clever hunter should be able
to return to his starting point."

229

Bill remembered what he had learned
about directions. From a clearing
in the woods, he looked up at the sky.

It was late afternoon. So he pointed
his right hand toward the sun in the west.
Then he knew which direction was south.

He might not be able to find George.
So he faced south and walked toward
Red Oaks. About dark he reached the edge
of town. There were George, Mr. Brooks,
and six other men coming toward him.

Mr. Brooks exclaimed, "We were starting
out to hunt for you! I know you're a
clever boy, but how did you find your way?
You must have been able to tell directions."

Bill said, "I couldn't go wrong!
This morning George showed me how
to find north, south, east, and west.
By going south, I was sure to find
Red Oaks. So here I am!"

Dick Whittington and His Cat

Long ago there was a poor boy named
Dick Whittington. He lived in a little
town not far from the city of London.
He had no father or mother. He had no one
to love him but his old gray cat.

Dick used to go from door to door asking
for something to eat. His cat would follow
him everywhere.

One day Dick heard some farmers talking.

One of them said, "London is a fine city.
One can find gold in the streets there."

"True," said another. "I've always
heard that about London."

Dick Whittington wanted to be rich,
anyway, a little richer than he was.

He said to his cat, "Let us go to London.
Surely it is a better place than this!"

"Meow!" said the cat, as if she wanted
to go. So they started out.

But when Dick got to the city of London,
he found no gold in the streets. He felt
more alone than ever before.

"I must get some work to do," he said.
"Working is better than being hungry."

"Meow," said the cat, as if she thought
so, too. Dick went from house to house,
looking for work. The cat followed him.

At last they came to the fine house
of a rich man.

Dick was just ringing the bell, when
the master of the house came out.
"Why are you ringing my bell?" he asked.

"I need some food for myself and my cat,"
said Dick. "I would like some work to do."

The rich man was sorry for Dick.
"I was a poor boy once myself," he said.
"You may stay here and help the cook."

So Dick stayed, but things were not much
better for him. The cook was not very kind,
and she gave him very little to eat.

One day the rich man called together
all the people who worked for him.

"I am sending a boat to faraway lands,"
he said. "If any of you want to send
something, my men will take it for you.
If people buy your goods, my men will
bring the money back to you in return."

Everyone but Dick had something to send.
"For myself, I have only my cat," he said.

"Well, then, send your cat," said the master.

Poor Dick was sorry to part with
his cat, but he wanted to send something.

"Very well, take her along," he said.

After this, things were harder for Dick
than ever before. At last he thought,
"London is no place for me. I will run away."

He started out, but then the bells of
London began to ring. They seemed to say,

"Turn again, Whittington,

And you shall be Mayor of London."

"Can the bells be ringing for me?" Dick
wondered. "Well, if I am to be Mayor
of London, I will go back." And he did.

Now, while this was happening, the boat
with Dick's cat landed in a strange country.

The boatmaster went to see the king, who
asked him to supper.

Just as they were about to eat, a number
of large rats jumped onto the table. They
ate up all the food.

"Oh, dear!" exclaimed the king. "The house
is filled with rats! There are rats in the
kitchen and rats in all the rooms. They
are not afraid of anything."

"Have you no cats?" the boatmaster asked.

The king had never heard of a cat. So the
boatmaster sent for Dick's cat. As soon as
she smelled rats, she began to chase them.
Soon she had caught nine of them. The rest
ran away as fast as they could.

"I must have that animal," said the king.
"I will fill your boat with bags of gold.
I will buy the rest of your goods, too."

So the boatmaster took the gold and
returned home. He went to the rich man's
house at once with a large bag of gold.

"Why, what is this?" asked the rich man.

"This is only part of what I got for
Dick Whittington's cat," said the boatmaster.
"Let us call him and show him the gold."

When Dick came in, his master smiled.
"Mr. Whittington!" he said. "Your cat
has made you rich."

So Dick was well off at last. When he
grew up, he was able to help the poor.

"I myself was once a poor boy," he said.

As it turned out, the bells were right.
The king heard of Dick and made him Mayor
of London. Three times he was Mayor, and
he was well loved. To this day people
of London remember Whittington and his cat.

Where the Brook Went

Peter Woods had always wondered
where the brook went. It passed
through the Woods's back yard.

Soon it changed its direction and ran
toward the east for a short way.
Then it turned toward the west.

The brook passed through Mr. Penny's
yard behind the henhouse. Then it turned
a third time and went toward the east again.

Peter could not imagine what its real
direction might be. "I'll find out
for myself where the brook goes," he said.
"I don't care how many miles I walk."

"I like your idea," said Betty.
"I'll follow the brook with you."

The next day the children walked for almost a mile along the edge of the brook. Part of the time they were in someone's back yard. Much of the time they seemed to be traveling toward the south.

The children could not imagine where the brook would take them.

Out in the country, about a mile from Red Oaks, there was a change in the brook. It grew deeper and ran faster. The sound it made seemed very loud.

Peter exclaimed, "How many miles does this brook go? Listen! It sounds almost as loud as a river now!"

A mile or so farther on, the children saw a bridge. At that point the brook met the rushing waters of a deep river.

A highway went over the bridge and passed a filling station near the river.

The children walked toward the station.

A young man met them at the door.
The children asked if they might have
a drink, and he brought them some water.

They both began to drink very fast.

"Don't drink too much," said the man.

"We have to fill up," joked Peter.
"Isn't this a filling station?"

"Yes," laughed the young man. "It's a
shop for fixing cars, too. I imagine
you might like to look around."

It wasn't long before the children saw
some horseshoes nailed above the door.

"Why are those horseshoes nailed on
the board above the door?" they both asked.

The man said, "I nailed them there
to help me remember that times change."

The young man went on, "Fifty years ago this was a blacksmith's shop."

"Were you the blacksmith?" asked Peter.

"No," answered the young man. "But my grandfather was. Grandfather made shoes for all the horses around here."

"Who fixed the cars?" asked Peter.

The young man laughed, "Fifty years ago there weren't any cars. People used wagons and teams of horses."

"How did your grandfather put shoes on a horse?" asked Betty.

"He would hold the shoe in the fire," said the young man. "A blacksmith had to wait until the shoe grew hot. Then he hammered it until it was just right."

"And after that?" asked Peter.

"The third step was to put it into cold water," said the young man. "Then the blacksmith nailed it onto the horse's foot."

The children asked more questions.

Both of them wanted to know if it hurt
a horse to have his shoes nailed on.

"No, it didn't," said the young man.
"A blacksmith would drive the nails
into the hard part of the foot. As he nailed
the shoe, he talked softly to the horse."

"Was your grandfather sorry when people
began to use cars?" questioned Betty.

The young man said, "You can't imagine
how sorry he felt. Grandfather loved
animals. He didn't like to see machines
take the place of horses."

A bell on the door started to ring loudly.
The grandfather came in to wash up.
He had been busy fixing a truck.

"Grandfather," called the young man. "Come here when you're through washing. Both the children have questions for you."

Then Peter asked, "Is it true you were once a blacksmith?"

"As true as true can be, child," laughed the grandfather. "But that was fifty years ago. Times have changed, and I've changed, too. Now I like machines."

Soon there was a loud sound in the sky. An airplane flew above the filling station.

"Hear that?" questioned the grandfather. "There will always be changes. Some day there might be an airport close by."

Peter exclaimed loudly, "And when I grow up, I'll have an airplane myself!"

The grandfather said, "Will you bring it here to be fixed? I imagine I can teach myself to fix airplanes. If times change, people should be able to change, too."

The Rich Goose

Once upon a time a rich goose walked
along carrying a heavy bag of corn.
On the road she met a robin.

"Hello, Mrs. Goose," called the robin.
"May I help you carry that heavy bag?"

"No, thank you," said the rich goose.
"I do not give my corn to anyone. This bag
is heavy, but I am able to carry it myself."

The robin said, "I know how you can
get more corn. First put your corn on the
ground. Then we can count the pieces."

Mrs. Goose put some corn on the ground.

But as fast as the clever robin counted
the pieces, he ate them. Then he flew
out of reach, laughing loudly.

"What a trick!" shouted Mrs. Goose.
She picked up her bag and went on.

Before long, Mrs. Goose met a crow.

The crow said, "I imagine you must be tired. You had better let me help you."

"No, thank you, Mr. Crow," she said. "It's better to carry my own riches."

But the clever crow said, "Let me teach you a game to make your corn grow."

"All right," said Mrs. Goose. "But be sure it isn't a trick, Mr. Crow!"

Then Mr. Crow said, "Make a magic ring on the ground with some of your corn. Then count the pieces. Your friend, Mr. Crow, will walk behind you and count them, too."

Mrs. Goose did as she was told, and they both began to count. But Mr. Crow ate as fast as he counted. He ate all the corn that was on the ground.

Mrs. Goose shouted at the crow, "The corn is gone! You tricked me!"

"Caw! Caw!" said the crow as he flew away.

"I've got to be more careful of my riches," thought Mrs. Goose. "One can never be too careful." So she tied up her bag.

She traveled along the river road for a mile. Then she met a river duck.

"What a heavy bag!" exclaimed the clever duck. "May I help you carry it?"

"No, thank you," answered Mrs. Goose. "I must be careful of my riches."

The river duck exclaimed loudly, "I'm a careful bird myself. And I'll tell you a secret. The fourth rock in the river is covered with pieces of gold."

"Gold on the fourth rock?" said the goose.

"Go and count it," said the river duck. "Your corn will be safe with me. I'll be careful to cover it with my feathers."

When Mrs. Goose reached the rock, there was not a piece of gold to be seen. When she returned, half her corn was gone.

Poor Mrs. Goose had only one fourth
of the corn she had started with. Now
her bag seemed as light as a feather.

"I must be careful of the few riches that
are left, or I shall be sorry," she thought.

So she decided that never again would
she let anyone take care of her corn.

Once more she carefully tied up her bag
and started down the road.

She met a hen who wanted some
corn for her children. She met a pig
who wanted to carry the bag for her.

"No, no," said Mrs. Goose. "My bag
is not heavy. I've decided that only
I myself shall carry it." And she went
on until she met a farmer's boy.

"Hello," he shouted. "I'll give you a
ride in my wagon. Hop up here by my side."

"Thanks," she said. "My legs are tired.
I should like to have a ride."

"What have you got in the bag?"
the boy questioned Mrs. Goose.

"All the corn I own," she answered.
"I have decided to keep it."

The boy said, "Why keep your corn
tied up? It is better to plant it.
Then the seeds will make more corn."

"Don't joke!" said Mrs. Goose.

"That is no joke!" said the boy.
"That is what we farmers do."

Mrs. Goose said, "Very well, then.
I've decided to let you plant it for me!"

In a few weeks the corn grew tall.
Then it was picked carefully.
Mrs. Goose got a bag of corn from
each seed that was planted.

What Do You Think?   Sequence

Who first tricked Mrs. Goose?
Who tricked her the third time?
Who was the second bird she met?
Who was the fourth?

A Wonderful Fourth of July

Four children stood on the corner
in front of Mr. Hammer's candy store.
Above the door was nailed an old signboard.
The strange old printed letters said

JOHN HAMMER

Country Store

"The same sign was over Mr. Hammer's
first store," said Betty, pointing to it.
"His first store stood here fifty years ago."

George couldn't imagine that.
"That's strange!" he exclaimed. "Was Red Oaks
here that long ago?"

"You must ask Mr. Hammer," said Betty.
"I imagine he can answer your question."

George thought it was a fine idea.

"Let's go in," he said.

And his sister Mary said, "We might
get some ice cream, too."

As they pushed open the door, a bell
made a loud sound. They took seats at the
counter and ordered ice cream with bananas.

Soon each child was busy eating.
But no one was too busy to ask questions.

Mary decided to ask the first question.
She said to Mr. Hammer, "Was there
a town of Red Oaks fifty years ago?"

"There was, child!" laughed Mr. Hammer.
"And mark what I say, we were proud of
our town. We all helped to build it."

"I have a question," said George.
"Did you own a candy store then?"

"I owned a country store,"
said Mr. Hammer. "It was the only store
for miles and miles around here."

Mr. Hammer said that his old store was
filled with everything you could imagine.
Wash goods, curtains, and bedcovers lay on
the counters. There were nails, plates,
and bags of flour. There were dresses,
caps, sewing machines, and washboards.

"I had seeds and cowbells in my store
then, too," he said. "This was farm
country fifty years ago. But fifty years
have brought many changes."

Betty asked a third question, "Did people
work hard then? Or did they have fun?"

"They did both," said Mr. Hammer.
"And if you don't believe me, I'll tell
you a true story about those times."

Mr. Hammer told the children about a
wonderful Fourth of July in Red Oaks.

"Imagine this town fifty years ago,"
he said. "That summer the railroad owners
decided to lay tracks this far west."

In those early days the town did not
have any fine buildings. It had no cars
or telephones or radios. It had no library
or moving-picture house.

It had only six houses, one store, and
a blacksmith shop a mile up the river.

There were no railroads, and there were
few roads. Farms a few miles away were
sometimes cut off from the town by storms.

All letters and newspapers were brought
by horse and wagon from Harbor City.
If the roads were wet, the trip took days.

So it seemed wonderful when it was
decided to lay railroad tracks to Red Oaks.
A railroad could bring in many things
and carry people to and from the city.

251

The first train would reach Red Oaks
at six o'clock on the Fourth of July.

The people decided to hold a party
on the Fourth of July. Everyone did
his part to get ready for the big day.

By noon on July the third, Red Oaks
looked as pretty as a picture. But in an
hour a heavy storm blew in from the east.

The strong east wind blew down trees and
took away roofs as if they were feathers.
Heavy rain followed the wind.

In half an hour the storm was over.
No one had been hurt, but the storm had
hit every home in Red Oaks. It had hit
the railroad, too. It had washed part
of the new tracks away.

Now the people wanted that railroad more
than anything. So the men decided to help
the railroad builders. They worked all
night and all next day to lay new tracks.

On the Fourth of July, at six o'clock, everyone waited near the railroad tracks.

Suddenly from far up the tracks came a whistling. A bell was ringing loudly, too. Those welcome sounds grew louder.

Then someone shouted, "Here comes our train. We did win after all!"

The people of Red Oaks decided it was the best Fourth of July they had ever seen.

"Why do you say that, Mr. Hammer?" asked George. "Didn't you have a storm?"

"Yes, we did," answered Mr. Hammer. "But the storm showed us we could count on each other. It made us better friends and neighbors, don't you see?"

"Oh, yes!" said George. "That's the best true story I've ever heard!"

What Do You Think? Main idea, relevancy

What Is the Story About?
The Building of Red Oaks   A Storm from the East
Good Friends and Neighbors

Study Pages

Sounds of Vowel Letters

Say the key word and its vowel sound. Then say the other words with the same vowel sound.

Key Word	Letters	Other Words

Two Sounds of **ow**

know	**ow**	crow, own, blow, grow
down	**ow**	clown, brown, cow, crowd

Two Sounds of **oo**

school	**oo**	moon, goose, noon, food
look	**oo**	brook, wood, stood, foot

Four Sounds of **ou**

out	**ou**	loud, count, south, proud
would	**ou**	could, should
country	**ou**	young, enough
thought	**ou**	brought

Two Sounds of **ea**

team	**ea**	teach, reach, east, real
head	**ea**	bread, feather, leather

Last Part s and es

Say **horse** and **horses.** How many parts
do you hear in each word? What is the first part
of **horses?**

Now say each underlined word
in the sentences that follow. Then say the first
part of each one.

1. Bananas come in <u>bunches.</u>
2. Sometimes <u>buses</u> make lots of <u>noises</u>
when they go over <u>bridges.</u>
3. The animal trainer <u>teaches</u> the lion in <u>cages</u>
to do tricks.
4. Goats sometimes jump over <u>fences</u> when
they want to go to new <u>places.</u>
5. When a boy <u>fixes</u> a clock he does not always
put the <u>pieces</u> in the right places.

What underlined word tells:
    where birds may live?
    what is left of a broken glass?

What Do You Think?

1. Freddie thinks that Green Hills is the best place to live.

This sentence tells you how Freddie feels about the town of Green Hills. Other people may not feel the same way.

2. The first building was put up in Green Hills fifty years ago.

This sentence tells you something about Green Hills that may be found in a book. Someone has printed the years when important things took place there.

Decide if the thought of each sentence that follows is like **1** or like **2**.

To the people of Green Hills, Mayor Gray was a wonderful man.

The first train stops in the Green Hills station at six o'clock in the morning.

Both buses and trains stop in Green Hills.

Green Hills is a town of pretty houses, stores, and office buildings.

Sounds You Know	New Words
One sound	
of **ow,** in **crow**	row, bowl
One sound	
of **oo,** in **food**	root
One sound	
of **ea,** in **east**	clean, dream

Parts You Know

u in **nut**
and **er** of **river**   butter
a in **rat**
and **er** of **river**   gather
e in **west**
and **y** of **heavy**   jelly
i in **rich**
and **ing** of **counting**   drifting

Find two things you like to eat on bread.

PHONIC SKILLS
AND
THINKING ABILITIES

Two types of direct and practical help are given in this section (pp. 254–277) of this storybook:

1. Introduction to phonic skills needed for identifying the vocabulary of the selections.
2. Introduction to thinking abilities required for the satisfactory comprehension of the selections.

Purposes

These activities serve two purposes:

1. *New skills.* For teaching new skills when they are needed
2. *Self help.* As a source of self help for the pupil

The sequence for teaching new skills and reviewing them is detailed in *The ABC Teacher's Guide: Second Reader (2–2)*. In addition, specific suggestions for teaching new skills are given in both the teacher's guide and the teacher's edition of this storybook, providing the busy teacher with practical help at the right time.

Use

Activities in this section of the book are used after the first (silent) reading of a selection. About three to five minutes are required for each one.

The phonics-thinking pages at the end of each unit of this book are used to:

1. Teach new phonic-thinking skills
2. Review learnings
3. Help the pupil to apply skills to selected words from the next unit.

For pupils who need additional help, these phonics-thinking pages may be used with one or more of the following:

Betts-Welch ABC Phonic Charts

Betts-Welch Study Book for *The ABC Over a City Bridge*

Pathways to Phonic Skills (recordings)

PHONIC SKILLS: AUTOMATIC USE

Children can be taught to use phonic skills and other word-learning skills automatically. When the use of these skills is automatic, pupils can then give their attention to the real purpose of reading: getting the thought.

Teaching New Skills

Teaching new phonic skills is done by having the pupils follow four easy steps:

1. Listen to the sound of the letter or syllable phonogram in the spoken word; e.g., the sound $ai\backslash\bar{a}\backslash$in *rain, wh* $\backslash hw\backslash$in *whistle,* or $a\backslash\partial\text{-}\backslash$in *afraid*
2. Say the vowel sound of the syllable
3. Identify the letters of the phonogram representing the sound or syllable
4. Check the use, or meaning, of the word in its sentence setting

Application of Skills

Teaching the *application* of phonic skills during silent reading-study activities is done by having the pupils:

1. Identify the unknown phonogram in the printed word
2. Recall the sound(s) represented by the phonogram
3. Identify the meaning of the word in its sentence

Specific suggestions for teaching the pupil to use his phonic skills automatically are given in the Teachers Edition: Annotated and Keyed.

THINKING

In this storybook, the thinking and phonic activities are carefully interwoven. For example, the study of last syllables *y* and *er* and compound words contributes to the pupil's (1) correct usage of words and (2) phonic skills.

Introducing New Learnings

This development of new learnings is done by having the pupil follow two steps:

1. Relate the purpose of the activity to the selection in this storybook
2. Complete the activity and identify—when practical—similar situations in the selection

Application of Learnings

New learnings are applied by the pupil during his silent reading and in activities following the silent and/or rereading. Silent and oral rereading afford many opportunities to interpret punctuation, discuss shifts of meanings, and make other applications.

CHILD LEARNINGS

This basic reading-study program helps the pupil (1) to mature in his *interests,* (2) to make automatic use of *phonic* skills and (3) to develop *concepts* and *thinking* abilities which insure comprehension. Detailed suggestions for achieving these goals are given in *The ABC Teacher's Guide: Second Reader (2-2).*

All previously taught skills are maintained in this book. (See Teacher's Edition: Annotated and Keyed.) New skills follow.

Phonics (letters and syllables)

1. Sounds of vowels with *r*, as *er (e)* \ar, er\ in *there; ear*\ ir\ in *year; or (e)*\ ōr, ȯr\ in *more; our*\ aùr\ in *flour; or*\ ȯr\ in *for; ire*\ īr\ in *fire*
2. Two sounds of *oo:* \ü\ as in *soon* and \u̇\ as in *stood*
3. Four sounds of *ou:* \aù\ as in *proud;* \ə\ as in *young;*\ u̇\ as in *would;* \ȯ\ as in *thought*

4. Two sounds of *ea:* \ē\ as in *teach;* \e\ as in *head*
5. Two phonograms for \ər\, as *ir* in *first* and *ur* in *turn*
6. Two phonograms for \au̇\ , as *ow* in *how* and *ou* in *proud*
7. Two phonograms for \ȯi\ as *oy* in *boy* and *oi* in *noise*
8. Sounds of *c,* as \k\ in *cage* and \s\ in *voice;* of *s* as \s\ in *send* and \z\ in *noise;* of *g* as \g\ in *got* and \j\ in *cage*
9. Silent consonants, as *t* in *listen, l* in *half, g* in *sign, h* in *hour*
10. Unstressed last syllable *s* and *es,* as in *fences* and *boxes*
11. Unstressed first syllable *be* \bə-\ as in *because*
12. Three last syllables—*ar, er or,*—with sound of \-r\, as in *dollar, master,* and *harbor*
13. Unstressed last syllable \-n\, as *en* in *sudden, in* in *robin, on* in *wagon, ain* in *curtain,* and *(i)on* in *station;* \-l\, as *le* in *uncle, el* in *travel*
14. Stressed syllables in two syllable words, as *mount* in *mounted; wake* in *awake*

Thinking

1. Punctuation: hyphen in compounds, as *high-school* boy; colon to signal an actor's lines in a play; single dash to signal an explanation of a preceding idea in a sentence
2. Use of homonyms, as *blue-blew*
3. Suffix *ly,* as in *gladly*
4. Relevant definitions of words
5. Statements relevant to paragraphs, etc.
6. Classification of ideas
7. Definite and indefinite terms, as *every, many, not one, a long way,* etc.
8. Context clues
9. Shifts in meanings and uses of words; e.g., *print, number*
10. Idiomatic expressions, as *follow orders*
11. Statements of fact (verifiable) versus opinion (expressions of attitudes)
12. Drawing conclusions: related facts; cause-effect

First Sounds: **f, l, fl; b, r, br; p, r, pr; s, t, st** (See Teacher's Guide for use of this page.)

| Pages 6–17 | Pages 18–35 | Pages 36–48 |

fire	jolly	floor
field	lot	lost
more	last	flash

harbor	roof	rock
build	round	brother
bear	cow	bright

Polaski	sail	present
noise	room	proud
people	rush	side

master	town	tall
soon	turn	station
sat	caught	still

Rhymes: **en, all, ay, ight** (See Teacher's Guide for use of this page.)

Pages 6–17   Pages 18–35   Pages 36–48

more

hen

when

then

men

side

men

hen

when

---

fall

place

call

call

all

fall

tall

rocks

call

gray

field

play

day

hay

stay

felt

day

gray

---

bridge

right

night

right

right

bright

night

floor

sad

track

cage

land

glad

Frank

a in at

bag

safe

track

need

met

felt

let

left

send

e in egg

get

test

sleep

side

Bill

bridge

ring

bring

string

i in it

smile

sing

still

rock

nos...

lot

not

got

clock

o in on

stop

rock

hole

cows___

horses___

tracks

cages

sides

houses

hills

noises

rings___

houses___

tricks

noses

strings

seats

places

chairs

goats___

cages___

crowds

holes

dances

voices

tests

bridges

rushed___

waited___

started

tracked

pulled

watched

needed

painted

talked___

seated___

landed

rocked

turned

started

helped

needed

pushed___

mounted___

learned

sailed

crowded

waited

tested

walked

Long and Short Sounds of a

The letter **a** has a short sound in the word **cat.** It has a long sound in the word **cage.** There is another vowel letter in **cage.** It is the last letter **e,** and it does not have a sound.

Find each word like **cage.** The long sound of **a** is heard, but the sound of **e** is not.

flash   brave   safe   game   glad

Long and Short Sounds of i

The letter **i** has a short sound in the word **pig.** It has a long sound in the word **pine.** There is another vowel letter in **pine.** It is the last letter **e,** and it does not have a sound.

Find each word like **pine.** The long sound of **i** is heard, but the sound of **e** is not.

smile   side   trick   while   bring

Long and Short Sounds of o

The letter **o** has a short sound in the word **rock.** It has a long sound in the word **rode.** There is another vowel letter in **rode.** It is the last letter **e,** and it does not have a sound.

Find each word like **rode.** The long sound of **o** is heard, but the sound of **e** is not.

close   hole   clock   got   nose

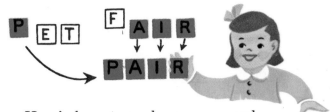

Here's how to make a new word.
Take the first letter of the word **pet.**
Then take the last three letters of **fair.**
Now say the new word.

Look at each word at the left.
Find two words at the right that help you
say that word.

| shop | show | top | pet |
| say | sing | gray | hope |

thump	bark	think	jump
frost	round	fruit	lost
brush	bright	four	rush
nut	near	cut	tall

well	told	wood	fell
block	blew	rock	king
dear	down	road	near
hop	been	hurt	shop

e in **egg**

need	test	
pet	sent	well
bed	step	tree
		met

i in **it**

trick	king	ice
while	think	which
his	swing	trip

o in **on**

hope	got	hop
top	not	home
shop	stop	block

u in **up**

you	cut	use
plum	brush	much
bunch	nut	nut

Last Sounds: **s, t, st; n, t, nt; n, d, nd; m, p, mp** (See Teacher's Guide.)

Pages 94–111   Pages 112–122   Pages 123–134

bus
fruit
yes

seat
sign
nut

frost
test
well

fell
pigeon
apron

sleep
pet
fruit

than
front
sent

listen
proud
lion

foot
bed
tried

been
kind
behind

from
plum
cut

step
tail
top

secret
jump
thump

You know many helps to new words.
Here are three of them. Read each one.
Then find the one you would use with
the new words that follow.

1. One vowel letter with a short sound,
   as in **well** and **hop**.
2. Two vowel letters, one with a long sound
   and an **e** with no sound, as in **ice**.
3. Rhymes, like **near** and **dear**.

Use one help to say each pair of words.

sun	milk	same	ball
can't	sit	five	call

near	bake	drink	drive
clear	joke	pond	fine

base	hit	half	grass
those	dig	wet	smell
love	park	ate	plant
glove	dark	woke	patch

ar in **far**

park

can't

hard

dark

hard

patch

March

March

car

barn

ear in **near**

dear

near

clear

wet

dear

near

sent

near

clear

year

or in **corn**

storm

short

soft

corn

horse

hop

for

corn

storm

horse

Put **er** on the word **sing,** and you have **singer.**
A singer is someone who likes to sing.

Find each word with **er.**

own   The owner of the store was out
         when Peter went in.

read   Betty is a good reader.

plant   The planter is busy planting seeds.

Put **er** on the word **warm,** and you have **warmer.**
The wind is warmer in May than it is in March.

Find each word with **er.**

clear   As the sky grows clearer, the sun
         gets brighter.

soft   This chair is softer than that one.

dark   George's coat is darker blue than
         Jimmy's coat.

small   A baby is smaller than a man.

strong   Jack is stronger than Ted.

short   This board is shorter than that one.

storm   kind   small

stormy   kindest   smaller

hilly

rocky

pick

rainy

Smith

frosty   Mr. Pottleby   A hunter caught

win   is a kind man.   a small rabbit.

He's the kindest Then he caught

man in town.   a smaller one.

soft   tall

softly   tallest

kindly   strongest   hunter

brightly   south   printer   **er**

young   shortest   poorest   **est**

bravely   coldest   younger   **ly**

lovely   mark   proudly   **y**

band   wrong   teacher

noon   warmest   stormy

ay in day

say	way		gray
hay	day		lay
cap	stay		pass
pay	may		say

ea in eat

team	seat		teach
real	read		reach
teach	bean		rest
bed	cream		real

oa in oak

boat	coat		rock
oak	road		goat
hot	oak		road
road	boat		coat

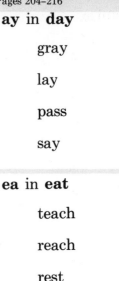

ou in out

found	out		mount
house	south		spot
shout	ground		proud
hop	mount		round

266

block	clock	print
pick	track	o'clock
Smith	trick	black
third	much	cook
which	teach	reach
teach	each	which
bus	finish	rush
push	flash	both
brush	fish	wash
swing	king	strong
soon	strong	bring
young	wrong	kitchen

267

First Sounds

change

clever

true

clear

chase

Rhymes

test

deep

west

might

sleep

Pages 231–253

Vowel Sounds

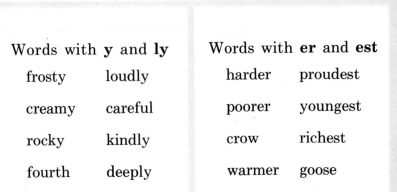

rich	short **a**	loud
bell	long **i**	part
rat	short **i**	sound
mile	long **e**	count
east	short **e**	mark

Words with **y** and **ly**

frosty	loudly
creamy	careful
rocky	kindly
fourth	deeply

Words with **er** and **est**

harder	proudest
poorer	youngest
crow	richest
warmer	goose

Are You Ready?

If you know the following, you are ready
for the next book.

1. What short vowel sound is heard in each word?

   rat　　　rich　　　west　　　cut　　　hot

2. What long vowel sound is heard in each word?

   mile　　　deep　　　chase　　　those　　　oak

3. What vowel letter is not heard in each word?

   face　　　side　　　nine　　　use　　　close

4. Which vowel is heard in each word?

   east　　　boat　　　lay　　　teach　　　goat

5. Say each word with the same first sounds.

   crow　　　true　　　cream　　　crowd　　　front

6. Say each word with the same last sounds.

   west　　　east　　　wash　　　frost　　　sound

7. Say each word with the last part **ly.**

   proudly　　kindly　　key　　　puppy　　　loudly

8. Find the first two letters and the last part
   of this new word: **skate.**

First letters:　　　sl　　　st　　　kn　　　sk

Last part:　　　　are　　　ate　　　ice　　　oak

Ted saw pigeons, blackbirds, and
other ___ in the park.

At the circus, he saw monkeys,
horses, bears, and other ___ .

birds
fish
animals

The children gave the horse some
apples to ___ .

Jack wished he could get some cold
water to ___ .

pull
drink
eat

"The country is no place to play,"
said the master. "It's a place to ___ ."

Jack said, "The country is all right
for country animals. But I guess I am
just a ___ horse."

city
work
farm

People ride to their floors of a high
building in a big ___ .

A city fireman rides to a fire in
a ___ .

truck
airplane
elevator

Where Is It?

Idiomatic Expressions
Pages 112-118

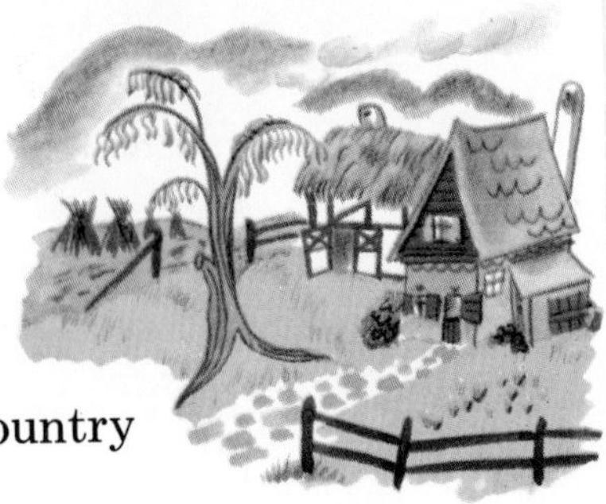

Mr. Polaski went back to the old country.

Did Mr. Polaski go back to a farm many years old?

No. He went back to the country where he first lived.

The policeman rode his mount up to the mayor.

Mrs. Bunch had a house to let.

The clown did not follow orders.

Concepts
Pages 119-122

Who is your uncle?

mother's father   father's brother   brother's father

What do you do when you remember?

think of something again

think of something lost

get a new thought

What comes after fall?

winter   spring   May

wood	Found under the bark of a tree
would	Was or were going to
write	To put down on paper
right	The other side of left, as **right** hand
blew	Did blow
blue	A color
road	A way on which cars travel
rode	Did ride
buy	To get by paying for
by	Near, close

The very first cars look funny to us now.
Their wheels were made of _____. They had no doors
on the left or on the _____ side. With no tops,
the wind _____ in. After a hard rain, they could not
go over a country _____. But some people now pay
a lot of money to _____ one of the funny old cars.

The sky turned from blue to black.

The wind began to blow.

Flashes of bright light cut across the sky.

All were signs of what?

Bill wanted to learn something new. He planted some seeds in two boxes. Then he waited for them to come up. After a few days of waiting and watching, he was happy to see the new green plants.

Over one box Bill put some paper to keep out the light. He left the top of the other box open. After a few days, he took the paper off the one box and found the plants white. But the plants in the open box were still green.

What did Bill learn?

What Happened—First, Second, Third, Last?

Jack Smith and his friends wanted to have their own school band.

First, they talked over the idea with their teacher, Mr. Barns. From him, they learned about many things they needed to do.

Second, they got the names of all the children who had said they would like to be in a band. After calling each one, they had seven people who said they would play.

Third, they found a good room for their use one hour a week. Here they could play as loudly as they wished. The noise would not be heard outside.

The young players worked hard every week. After six weeks, they were ready to play for the other children. After the show was over, they were told it could not have been better. At last, Jack and his friends had their own school band. It was a good one. too!

Bill runs fast.

Fast tells how Bill runs.

Bill runs faster than Jack.

Faster tells how two boys run.

Bill can run the fastest of all.

Fastest tells how one of three or more boys runs.

Polly had a white coat and Betty had a blue coat.

Which girl had the ____ coat?

dark
darker
darkest

At the circus Bill and Frank saw a lion, a goat, and a woodchuck.

Which animal was the ____ ?

strong
stronger
strongest

Jack was four feet tall. Ted was four and one-half feet tall. Joe was more than five feet tall.

Which boy was the ____ ?

short
shorter
shortest

What Are They Called?

school, barn, library money

trees, grasses, flowers clothes

hour, minute, second plants

penny, dollar buildings

glove, apron, coat time

east, west, north, south order

first, second, third directions

apple, banana, plum animals

shoemaker, fireman, policeman workers

pigeon, cow, lion, reindeer fruit

five, four, six, seven sounds

morning, noon, evening numbers

beans, nuts, cake, milk, plums colors

gray, yellow, green, blue time

bark, ringing, thump, whistling food

THE $\mathcal{ABC}$ Over a City Bridge

NEW WORDS: 229

TOTAL VOCABULARY FOR *The ABC Down Singing River*
AND *The ABC Over a City Bridge:* 412

CUMULATIVE VOCABULARY: 719

The ABC Over a City Bridge follows the series *The ABC On Our Way, The ABC Time to Play, The ABC All in a Day, The ABC Up the Street and Down, The ABC Around Green Hills,* and *The ABC Down Singing River.*

The ABC Over a City Bridge and the accompanying study book introduce and develop the 412 words listed below.

A unique program for developing and extending phonic and thinking skills is given on pages 254–277 of the book. In addition, the ABC Phonic Charts and Pathways to Phonic Skills (recordings) may be used for both individualized and group activities.

Specific suggestions for using this book and the accompanying study book are given in the Teacher's Guide.

The vocabulary chart below indicates the page on which each of the 229 new words is introduced in *The ABC Over a City Bridge.* Each of the 183 words used in *The ABC Down Singing River* is indicated by an asterisk (*). These words are introduced and maintained as "new" words in this book.

All variants of a word, with the exception of those ending in *s, 's, s', d, ed, es, ing, er* (comparison), and *est,* are counted as new words. Contractions in which one letter is omitted are not counted as new words. In addition, exceptions are made for compounds of two known words and for words ending in the suffixes *y, er* (agent), and *ly.*

UNIT I	20. stairs	34. suddenly	48. good-by
	21. happen*	rushed	
5. city*	22. Mary*	35.	UNIT II
6. bridge*	brother	36. side	
harbor	23. George*	flash	49. . . . .
7. afraid	pigeons	37. still*	50. whistling
building*	24. every*	need*	Bill*
8. fire*	sailed*	38. bright	heard*
9. noise*	25. jolly	proud	51. Frank*
10. wagon*	answered*	39. rocks*	whistle
11.	26. light*	tall	52. cage
12. Polaski	pulled*	fix*	open*
field*	27. cows	40. felt*	53. flew
13. elevator*	caught	41.	an*
room*	28. round	42. present*	54. listened
14. gray	29. met*	windows	55. never*
more	30. bus*	43. floor*	56. mountains
15. thought*	turning*	dollars	through*
master	31. across	44. few*	57. sad*
place*	stood*	moving	follow*
16.	32. boats*	45. police*	58. start
17.	men*	minutes	blew
18. roof*	33. while	46. lost	59. wait*
aunt*	watch*	47. station*	tracks
19.			

60. . . . .
61. brave
    any*
62. always*
    tried
63. because
    ring
64. left*
    tricks
65. lion*
    hurt*
66. tail*
    smile*
67. birthday
    airport
68. close*
    land*
69. . . . .
70. behind
    bring
71. wonderful*
    gives*
72. send*
    pay
73. money*
    seven*
74. marionette
75. library
    got
76. seat
    strings
77. . . . .
78. tables*
    chairs*
79. found*
    glad*
80. goats*
    wolf
    safe*
81. voice*
82. cream*
    supper*
83. flour
    hungry*
84. sleeping*
    hole
85. mounted
    crowds*
86. rode*
    learn*
    told*
87. tests
    alone*
    hard
88. push
89. orders
    important

90. remember
91. sing*
    above
92. travel*

UNIT III

93. shops*
94. uncle*
    fruit
    pet*
95. plums
    bananas
96. bunch
    swing
97. care*
    fell*
98. top*
99. himself
    say*
100. shoemaker
    hope*
    think*
101. early*
    cut
    mayor
102. why*
    apron
103. foot*
    near*
104. sew
    hammer
105. . . . .
106. elves
    enough*
107. leather
    pair
108. finished*
    four*
109. wife*
    bed*
110. tiny
    warm*
111. evening*
    step*
112. Bingo
    thumped
113. papers*
    apartment
114. should*
    kind
115. write*
    keep*
116. sent
    sign
117. front
    barked*

118. . . . .
119. frost
    king*
    winter*
120. welcome
    covering
121. brush
    nuts
122. magic*
    I'll*
123. Christmas*
    wood*
    much
124. John*
    Santa Claus*
    believe
125. secret*
126. reindeer
    than
127. well
    until*
128. block
129. dear
    trips
130. ice*
    which
131. before*
    hop
132. use*
    key
133. been*
    puppy
134. or
    family*

UNIT IV

135. . . . .
136. oak
    picture*
137. five*
    own
138. sun*
    carry*
    ahead
139. telephone
140. hurry*
    drive*
    farther
141. along*
142. . . . .
143. corner
    Peter
144. March
    patch
    clothes*
145. Betty*
    milk*

146. sit*
    balls*
147. almost*
148. same
    can't*
149. storm
    nothing*
    clear
150. drink*
    sure
    bread
151. beans
152. busy*
    food
153. radio
154. corn*
    baked
155. read*
156. woodchuck*
    joke
    fisherman*
157. fine
    pond
158. moon
    try
159. once*
    ground
160. only*
    sky*
161. seeds*
    together
162. glove
    base
163. small*
    hit
164. plants*
    half
165. dig
    soft
    hour*
166. those
167. grass
168. . . . .
169. Bozo
    eyes
170. woke*
    strong*
171. smell
    strange
172. loved
    paws*
173. ate*
    neighbor*
174. dark
    board
175. seen*

279

176. tired
    edge
177. piece*
178. short*
179. wet
180. . . . .

UNIT V
181. . . . .
182. Saturday
    pick
183. ago*
    hear
184. cap*
    teach
185. sisters*
    empty
186. large*
    real
187. Smith
    young*
188. teams*
    second
189. nine
    win
190. third
191. ever*
    hot*
    noon
192. . . . .
193. band
    shouted
194. tied

195. robin
    south
196. leg*
    mark
    feathers
197. office*
    number
198. air
    north
199. Pottlebys
    child
200. poor*
    dress*
    suit
201. wrong
    wear*
202. machine
    curtains
203. knew*
204. summer*
    reach*
    o'clock
205. hunt
    wonder
206. passed
    lunch
207. printed
208. both
    rest
209. . . . .
210. . . . .
211. six
    cooking

212. plates
    lay
213. kitchen*
214. gone
215. wash
    cake*
216. I've*
    brought*
UNIT VI
217. . . . .
218. change*
    heavy
219. idea
    chased
220. deep
    sorry
    grew*
221. face*
    seemed
222. . . . .
223. true
    return
224. might
    part
225. sound
    exlaimed
226. direction
    pointed
227. east
    west
228. able
    toward
229. clever*

230. . . . .
231. Whittington
    London
232. rich
    better
233. bell
    myself
234. . . . .
235. rats
    filled*
236. . . . .
237. imagine
    miles
238. loud
    river*
239. nailed
240. fifty
    grandfather
241. questions
242. . . . .
243. goose
    count
244. crow
245. careful
    fourth
246. decided
247. . . . .
248. July
249. . . . .
250. railroad
251. . . . .
252. . . . .
253. . . .

PHONICS: Pages 254–269
THINKING ACTIVITIES: Pages 270–277

ACKNOWLEDGMENTS

Grateful acknowledgment is made for permission to adapt and use the following copy-righted material:
"Mr. Plum and the Little Green Tree" adapted from *Mr. Plum and the Little Green Tree* by Helen Earle Gilbert, copyright 1946 by Stone and Pierce and published by Abingdon Press; used by permission of the publishers.
"Bozo" and "A Long Winter Sleep" from *Bozo the Woodchuck* by Dorothy Lothrop Brown and Marguerite Butterfield; used by permission of American Book Company.
"The Tree House" by Elinor Skelly, suggested by stories from *Fun in Town and Country* by Eleanor L. Skinner; used by permission of American Book Company.
"The City Horse" from *The Horse Who Lived Upstairs* by Phyllis McGinley. Copyright 1944 by Phyllis McGinley and Helen Stone. Reprinted by permission of the author and Curtis Brown, Ltd.
"A Letter from Santa Claus" from "A Letter from Santa" by Mary Graham Bonner in *Jack and Jill*; used by permission of the author.
"No-Whistle" by Polly Curren, reprinted from May 1947 *Jr. Language and Arts,* by permission of Progressive Educators, Inc.

280